THE NATURE OF ANIMALS

THE
NATURE
OF
ANIMALS

❀ ❀ ❀

Lorus and Margery Milne

Illustrated by Thomas R. Funderburk

J. B. Lippincott Company

PHILADELPHIA NEW YORK

591
M

Contents

THE NATURE OF ANIMALS

CHAPTER

I

The Sizes and Shapes of Animals

By the time a great blue whale is two years old, it is already larger than any other kind of animal. It weighs more than fifty tons, surpassing its modern competitors the basking sharks and whale sharks. A three-year-old blue whale may have a length of 77 feet. An 89-foot individual tipped the scales at a hundred and nineteen tons. And blues a full 109 feet in length have been caught. They far exceeded in size even those extinct giants, the mighty dinosaurs.

Near the opposite extreme in animal dimensions is the malaria parasite carried by mosquitoes. This parasite enters a single red blood cell of a person bitten by an infected mosquito, and gains enough nourishment in the flattened disk to spawn a horde of new individuals. The mosquito that carries malaria is a hundred millions times as bulky and heavy as a malaria parasite. The average human being weighs as much as a hundred million mosquitoes.

For centuries, the diminutive malaria parasite has been affecting the fortunes of mankind, perhaps more than any

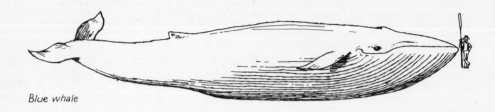

Blue whale

other animal has done. Through destruction of red blood cells and release of poisons into the blood stream, it saps man's energy, makes him susceptible to other diseases, and often limits the areas in which his civilizations can thrive. Yet the tiny parasite itself has features in common with the great blue whale. Both of them survive only while supported by a liquid—the sea in the one instance, blood or a mosquito's saliva in the other. Moreover, the malaria parasite is a cell, the whale a wonderful population of cooperating cells.

The malaria parasite, the great blue whale and all the rest of the animal kingdom face essentially the same fundamental needs. Each of them requires oxygen, water, and food. Each must rid itself of wastes, avoid enemies, repair damages, find mates, reproduce and disperse new generations. Every kind of animal meets these necessities in its own way, with its own specializations.

No one type of animal has the best solution to all the fundamental problems. Each is a compromise, combining gains and losses. Any one body plan or behavior or localized living space differs in many details from all others. In these differences we may see a way to distinguish between the various kinds of animals.

Today more than 882,000 unlike types of animals are known. Hundreds of still anonymous kinds are discovered every year, and given names. About 30,000 remain single cells for life as does the malaria parasite. Many of these never grow large enough to be visible to the unaided human eye. A few of them, such as the slipper animalcule *Paramecium*, attain a length of $\frac{1}{100}$ of an inch—a hundred and fifty times the size of a human red blood cell. A person with good eyesight can detect slipper animalcules as motes cruising slowly about in stagnant water that is brightly lit.

When seen through the microscope, a paramecium shows many features found in other animal cells. It consists of a single mass of living material (protoplasm) bounded by a thin, flexible but firm outer layer called the cortex. Protoplasm, the sole embodiment of life, is chiefly water. It gains its living character through the elaborate organization of less abundant chemical compounds. Huge molecules of proteins, although relatively few in number, appear to have the assistance of smaller molecules of fats in controlling the protoplasmic water, in absorbing a host of simple substances from the surrounding world, and in managing the carbohydrates (starches) stored as food reserves.

Gradually the protoplasm acquires from outside the cell the assortment of dissolved substances important in survival. Among these are oxygen and minerals used in cellular chemistry. Carbon-containing compounds must be taken in, and then broken down to yield the energy for life. All animal cells must do this. In the last analysis, all of them are dependent upon green plants which alone can capture the energy of sunlight and incorporate it into carbon-containing compounds.

An animal cell may get its food directly by eating green plants, or obtain it at second hand in other kinds of nourishment. A paramecium captures minute bacteria far smaller than itself, and digests the bacterial cells. Thereby each paramecium acquires the energy-rich compounds the bacterium obtained while causing the decay of a dead green plant.

Only protoplasm can build more protoplasm. The blueprints for the essential proteins and fats and chemical reactions are bound up in a special part of the living organization, the nucleus. Not only does the nucleus control the activities of the remaining protoplasm (the cytoplasm) and of

the cell as a whole, but it also attends to the accurate duplication of the blueprints. It parcels them out into a pair of
identical packages when the cell grows large enough to divide into two individuals. Each daughter cell receives a complete nucleus, containing the full heritage of that particular
kind of animal.

By comparison with a malaria parasite, a paramecium is
a very fancy cell. The flexible cortex in the shape of a
slipper is set with row after row of minute extensions resembling hairs. These are not adornments but cilia, with
which the protoplasm can lash at the pond water and drive
the whole cell along on a spiral course, to more and more
bacteria. A delicate network of special protoplasm just inside
the cortex links the cilia and coordinates their beating into
an efficient rhythm, like waves of activity sweeping over the
cell. It is the counterpart of a nervous system inside a single
unit of protoplasm, and allows a paramecium to reverse its
direction of swimming when an obstacle is encountered, to
rotate slowly, and then dash off in a new direction.

A broad groove in a paramecium's cortex ends in a small
hole, a pore through which special cilia can slap a collection
of bacteria in a bit of water into the cell's interior. There the

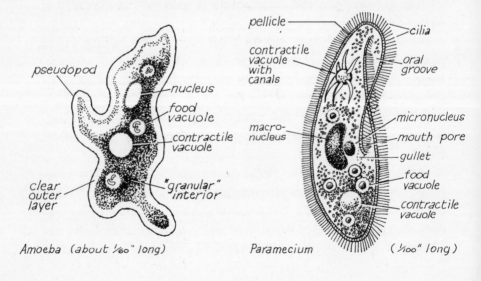

Amoeba (about 1/60" long)   Paramecium   (1/100" long)

water forms a spherical drop enclosing the food particles. Slowly the protoplasm shifts the drop and its cargo on a long path resembling a figure eight. Along this course within the cell, the protoplasm secretes digestive ferments into the water drop, changing its chemical nature. Products of digestion pass into the protoplasm. Any indigestible residues remain in the water drop until it is thrust out at the end of the figure eight course, pushed into the pond through another pore in the cortex.

Other evidences of internal complexity are often visible toward the two ends of a slipper animalcule. A pattern of short canals appears, like the radiating parts of an asterisk (*). Suddenly these transparent lines touch at the center and open out into a sphere, which grows in size. At a critical moment the sphere contracts to complete obliteration. This sphere is a contractile vacuole which has collected excess water from the protoplasm and discharged it to the outside world through still another pore in the cortex. It is a paramecium's means for surviving in fresh water, which penetrates the cortex and diffuses through the protoplasm. In brackish ponds, less water enters the cell and the contractile vacuoles can work more slowly or disappear altogether.

The malaria parasite shows many features of other animals, but also has its own specializations. It gets its water from the blood or saliva it lives in, and can absorb the oxygen it needs just as simply as a paramecium does from a pond. The parasite lets man capture its food and digest it, then removes from his blood the materials it needs. It rides from man to man in a mosquito, and from skin to liver or bone marrow in the human blood stream. One red blood cell contains everything a malaria microbe requires, and somehow the parasite's protoplasm flows into the blood cell it attacks without leaving any hole. Only after the invader has destroyed the contents of the blood cell and reproduced there, does the red cell swell and burst, freeing more parasites and a fever-inducing poison into the blood stream.

Animals of many shapes follow the unicellular way of life and gain from it certain advantages in small size. Thus when a pond dries out, multitudes of parameciums lose a little water, round themselves up and secrete a heavy covering. They can then be blown by the wind as dust particles, with a chance of falling into another pond, there to start a new life.

The scientist looks with wonder at microscopic cells because they have so much area in proportion to their weight. A paramecium, for example, is not too different in shape from the average fish. Now, the total surface area of a six-inch fish might be no more than 20 square inches. But the same weight of living protoplasm, swimming around in bits the size of a paramecium, would have a total surface area of 20,000 square inches!

The weight of an animal, whether it is a fish or a paramecium, is an indication of its needs for food and oxygen. The surface is the area where the animal is in contact with the world around it, and through which its oxygen and food must come. A paramecium attends to respiration through its surface with no apparent effort and no specializations, whereas a fish must continually gulp water and create a current through its delicate gills.

As smaller and smaller cells are examined, the surface grows ever more impressive in proportion to weight. New limitations are encountered, too. A paramecium is only about a thousand times larger than the largest protein molecule in protoplasm. A cell less than a hundredth the length of a paramecium may not have enough space inside to accommodate all of the different large protein molecules needed by an active animal reacting to its environment. Moreover, a creature so small is buffeted by movements of molecules in the surrounding pond or sea, and has difficulty traveling about on its own. In the air it could not be active, for through its relatively enormous surface its scant store of moisture would evaporate, promptly bringing to a halt the chemical processes in its protoplasm.

In the direction of larger sizes, the unicellular way of life reaches frontiers, too. As a cell grows, the weight of protoplasm demanding food and oxygen becomes too large for feeble cilia to propel from place to place. The surface becomes too small in proportion to weight unless it is stretched out in a flat disk or extended into a radiating pattern like a Christmas star. To achieve this spreading of the protoplasm, increasing its surface area, a skeleton seems to be necessary.

The famous chalk cliffs of Dover in England are the remains of countless unicellular animals that absorbed calcium salts from the sea and built a shell-like framework of lime. Fingers of protoplasm reached out through minute holes in the framework. These holes cause the empty shells to resemble white palaces with windows, the openings for which the Foraminifera [window-bearers] are named. Among fossil Foraminifera, a few as much as one inch in diameter have been found, their wafer-thin shells intact after millions of years.

Skeletons shaped like Christmas stars arose among another group of unicellular animals, the radiolarians. These creatures take from sea water the infinitesimal traces of silica—the "insoluble" substance of sand—and secrete slender glassy needles upon which the protoplasm extends in a multitude

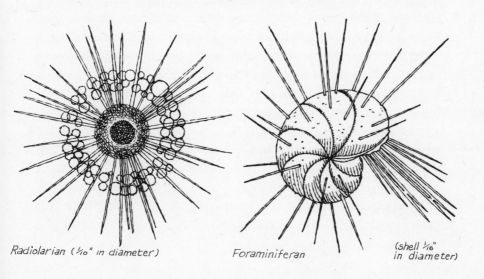

Radiolarian (1/10" *in diameter*)   *Foraminiferan*   (shell 1/16" in diameter)

of directions. Cross connections between the radiating needles give the skeleton rigidity and permit the living animal to expand as a thin coating over a latticework as exquisite as a snowflake. On its glassy support, the radiolarian resembles a three-dimensional spider web, reaching out sticky protoplasm as a trap for bacteria and other minute particles of food. Although some of these radiolarian cells attain a diameter as great as ¼ of an inch, only a little of this volume is occupied by protoplasm.

Animals with Many Cells

Many of the limitations encountered by single cells are avoided if a number of cells cooperate, working one for all and all for one, as a multicellular individual. Most kinds of animals show this organization. Usually just a few cells attend to reproduction, while all of the others slowly grow old and die. By contrast, in unicellular life each single cell is a potential parent. When it divides into two daughter cells, no aging individual remains; both daughters are juveniles.

For a multicellular animal to be successful, each cell must relate its activities to those in all neighboring cells. Every cell must be sensitive to chemical substances produced by those neighbors, and alter its own living functions in relation to theirs. At the same time, it must be able to signal to the neighbors, producing chemical substances to which they are sensitive. The compounds that serve as messages are hormones, an essential feature of multicellular life.

About 4,500 different kinds of sponges demonstrate how simple a multicellular animal can be. Sponge cells become specialized into one of four types, but never lose their ability to cease particular duties in the colony and transform, taking over tasks of another cell type. Each sponge cell becomes either flattened as part of the surface of the sponge colony, or doughtnut-shaped as a pore cell through which water can pass from the outside world to a central cavity, or equipped

with a water-moving whiplash (flagellum) and a food-catch-
ing collar of sticky protoplasm extending into the central
cavity, or a sort of general utility cell moving about among
all the others.

The sponge colony rests on the bottom of the sea or stream,
and drives water through its pore cells to the cavity and
then into the outside world. During this passage, the water
brings the sponge particles of food which the collar cells
capture; it carries oxygen to the sponge and takes away dissolved wastes. Meanwhile the general utility cells act as wait-
resses, distributing the food to all cells, or cooperate as little
groups in secreting a skeleton.

Some sponges produce needles of lime, wedged together in
a fashion to provide support and at the same time discourage
animals that might chew on the sponge. The bath sponge
and many others create an elaborate meshwork of a plastic
substance so fine in texture that it will hold quantities of
water even after the sponge cells die and disintegrate. This
plastic skeleton is flexible, and seems adequate for the largest sponges, some of them greater in diameter than a basket-
ball. In deeper, calmer seas, still other sponges create delicate
skeletons of glass, firmly built into a continuous fabric supporting the living cells where they can reach food-filled water.
The skeleton of the Venus' flower-basket sponge is often
cleaned and displayed for its beauty in a museum case.

Animals with Tissues

All multicellular animals except sponges have their cells
grouped into layers called tissues. About 9,600 different kinds
of animals get along with only two cellular layers—an outer
and an inner—in a body as radially symmetrical as a daisy.
Between the two layers the cells secrete a nonliving jelly,
the material from which the jellyfish gets its name.

Jellyfishes include a few giant kinds. One of them in
northern seas is *Cyanea arctica,* a great broad bell as much

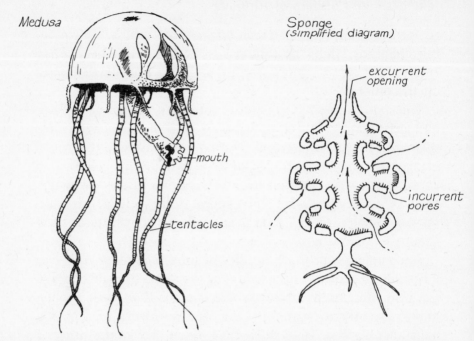

Medusa

mouth

tentacles

Sponge
(simplified diagram)

excurrent
opening

incurrent
pores

as seven feet across and eighteen inches thick, hung all around with bulky tentacles at least five feet long. Most horses bulk no larger, and the giant jellyfish must weigh at least half a ton. Scientists call jellyfishes medusae.

By feeble contractions, a jellyfish swims along, buoyed up by the surrounding water. Special cells in the outer layer over its trailing tentacles sting and cling to any small animals colliding with them. Slowly the jellyfish thrusts these victims through a mouth located centrally below the bell, and into an umbrella-shaped digestive cavity. Residues are spat out again.

Smaller members of the group to which the jellyfish belongs (the coelenterates) include the flowerlike sea anemones, the coral animals, and others which attach themselves to the bottom. There they may secrete elaborate skeletons, holding their bodies where the tentacles can reach successfully for food. These skeletons are familiarly known as sea fans and corals, some of which form reefs and inhabitable islands in tropic seas. Most of these animals are sociable, living in great colonies, each individual member contributing to the common edifice. They cannot live on land or tolerate long exposure to dry air. Yet their way of life can be as fascinating as any in the animal kingdom. Scientists call them hydroids.

All other multicellular animals have at least three layers of cells; they acquire a distinction between a right-hand side and a left, and advancing (anterior) end and a retreating (posterior) end—the marks of bilateral symmetry.

This division of labor and complexity of body are not limited to animals of large size. Among the most delightful denizens of pond water are the microscopic wheel animalcules or rotifers, many of them far smaller than a paramecium, although they are composed of more than a hundred cells. Each rotifer can swim along, propelled by a ring of cilia that gives the illusion of a rotating wheel. Or it can use the secretion from cement glands to glue its two narrow toes temporarily to the bottom. Meanwhile a complicated grinding mill inside the diminutive body crushes bacteria and algal cells as food, in a digestive tract extending through the body from end to end. Rotifers take advantage of their small size by becoming windblown dust particles when the pond dries up. Few larger animals can use this effortless method of transportation and become so cosmopolitan.

If success in life is measured by the number of unlike environments an animal can duplicate, the laurel might well go to the 10,500 kinds of nematode worms. After a lifetime spent studying nematodes, Dr. N. A. Cobb of the United States National Museum wrote of these simply built, slender, wriggling creatures:

If all the matter in the universe except the nematodes were swept away, our world would still be dimly recognizable, and if, as disembodied spirits, we could then investigate it, we should find its mountains, hills, vales, rivers, lakes, and oceans represented by a thin film of nematodes. The location of towns would be decipherable, since for every massing of human beings there would be a corresponding massing of certain nematodes. Trees would still stand in ghostly rows representing our streets and highways. The location of the various plants and animals would still be decipherable, and, had we sufficient knowledge, in many cases even their species could be determined by an examination of their erstwhile nematode parasites.

A nematode's body, seldom longer than half an inch, is like a pair of tubes one inside the other, joined only at the ends—at mouth and anus. Food passes through the inner tube and the products of digestion are absorbed into a blood-like liquid lying in the space between the two tubes. Whenever the worm bends, the liquid shifts, thus carrying nourishment from one part of the body to another.

With few specializations except in habits, the nematodes have come to be among the most important worms in soil, living as parasites at the expense of most larger kinds of animals and plants. The hookworm is a nematode, and so are the pinworm, the trichina worm of undercooked pork, and the parasite that causes elephantiasis.

Animals That Shed Their Skeletons

If success is measured, instead, by the number of different kinds of animals following a common body plan, then the great group Arthropoda would definitely win the prize. It includes some 25,000 types of crustaceans, 29,000 members of spiders, and over 660,000 known kinds of insects. The insects alone outnumber the rest of the animal kingdom by two to one.

Arthropods live in jointed shells of their own secretion. They fly or walk or swim or creep, on wings or legs of similar construction. To grow, they must shed the old shell and let a new one harden in larger size. Yet this body plan is found in tiny wasps scarcely larger than a paramecium, as well as in six-inch beetles such as *Titanus giganteus* of Brazil, or

extinct dragonflies with a 29-inch wingspread, or tree-climb-
ing, coconut-eating robber crabs of the South Pacific reaching a weight of twenty pounds, or the giant spider crab of
Japanese waters whose outspread pincers span as much as
nine feet.

So numerous are the arthropods, whether as crustaceans
in the seas and fresh waters or as insects and spiders on
land, that they probably exceed in total weight of living protoplasm all other kinds of animals combined. The crustaceans
transform green plants into food useful to larger aquatic
animals. The insects do the same in fresh water and on
land. Without arthropods the giant jellyfish, the great whale
sharks and basking sharks, and the whalebone whales could
not survive, for they eat almost nothing else. Without in-

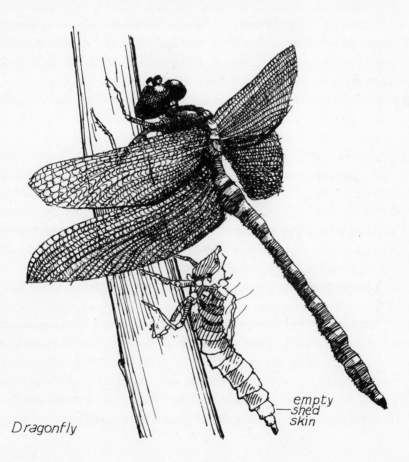

Dragonfly

empty
—shed
skin

sects, most of the amphibians, such as frogs and toads, would starve. And it is doubtful whether the world would ever have had reptiles, birds, mammals, or flowering plants if insects had not appeared on earth. All these animals came on the scene only after insects had multiplied; all the early land vertebrates were insect-eaters, and flowers have little meaning except in attracting the insects that pollinate them, thus insuring the plant will reproduce.

Animals with Backbones

By comparison with 772,000 different types of arthropods, the vertebrate animals and the mollusks seem insignificant. The vertebrates—animals with backbones—total only about 45,000 kinds. A third of them are fish, a third mammals, the rest mostly amphibians, reptiles and birds. The smallest of them when adult include a tropical fish and a jungle frog, each about half as large as a honeybee. Both of these pygmies depend upon arthropods as food.

Birds and mammals long ago achieved the ability to maintain a fairly constant blood temperature; they became "warm-blooded," setting themselves off from the rest of the animal kingdom. In a cold-blooded creature, the body temperature rises and falls with that of their surroundings. This gain by animals with feathers or fur permits them to be active in cold weather. It limits them as well. If they live in the Arctic, they cannot have prominent ears or long tails, for in winter the heat loss from these projections would be excessive, requiring extra food, which is hard to find.

Even in the tropics, a warm-blooded animal cannot be smaller than a certain size. On a cool night the least of birds (a hummingbird) and of mammals (a shrew) lose so much heat that their lives are endangered. Animals of this size cannot hibernate or even spend a week in inactivity. They must rush about for much of every day, obtaining perhaps half their own weight in quick-energy food, merely to stay alive. Too small a body cannot digest food fast enough and produce

Red fox   Arctic fox

heat as rapidly as it is lost through the relatively enormous body surface.

The restless shrew, by being smaller than a big beetle, suffers from too much surface. The active beetle, by being larger than a small mouse, has a body clamoring for more oxygen than its branching system of breathing tubes can deliver. It must stumble about in thick armor as disproportionately heavy as the skeleton of an elephant. The giant *Titanus* beetle has good wings, but no one yet knows whether the insect uses them for flying about. The elephant has sturdy legs, but never uses them to run or jump. The skeleton of each has grown close to its limit of mechanical strength, and strains upon it could be disastrous.

The Mollusks

About 40,000 different kinds of mollusks roam the world. Most of them withdraw into their shells whenever they are threatened; they cease activity until the danger passes. They wear a protective limy shell and live on the bottom of sea or lake as clams and oysters do, or they creep about with the habits of snails. Slugs manage with little or no shell, but they can survive only where they can find moist hiding places. None of these animals can be active in dry air. Only when under water are they active in full sunlight.

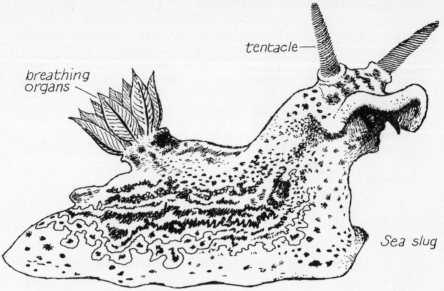

tentacle—

breathing
organs

Sea slug

A snail has a spiral, one-piece shell, whereas a clam's covering is in two symmetrical halves hinged together. The smallest snails and clams are often carried from place to place embedded in the mud on the feet of wading birds. The largest marine snails are the horse conch of Atlantic coasts from North Carolina to Brazil and an Australian variety; both produce a 24-inch shell. On land, the giant of snails is a denizen of the African jungles, particularly in Liberia; its shell reaches eight inches in length and four in diameter. The largest clams live in reefs of the South Pacific, where they reach a weight of half a ton or more.

Distant cousins of the clams and snails are the squids and cuttlefish, the octopus and pearly nautilus. Most of them have dispensed with a protective shell and lead aggressive lives. With sucker-studded tentacles they capture crabs and fish. Tremendous eyes, resembling those of vertebrates, stare from the streamlined body of a squid or a cuttlefish as it hovers, firm fins pulsing, or dashes off by jet propulsion. These are the "head-footed" mollusks (the cephalopods) which live at all depths in the ocean and battle vigorously with the sharks, fishes, seals, and toothed whales that prey upon them.

The giant squid *Architeuthis* is the largest of all invertebrates, or animals without backbones. This monster reaches a length of at least ten feet and a diameter of three, with 40-foot tentacles and an eye 15 inches across. A giant squid can weigh more than three tons. Its large and well-developed brain seems to make the animal a fair match for the killer whales and cachalots.

Sperm whales of Moby Dick's kind find far larger squids than man has met. Enormous scars the size of dinner plates are found on the heads of whales, showing where the suction cups on the tentacles of a giant squid once held while the animal wrestled for its life. And in whale stomachs have been found the parrotlike beaks of squids much bigger than any that have been discovered among the rare dying giants cast by storms upon the shore. Some day the sea may reveal just how big a squid can grow.

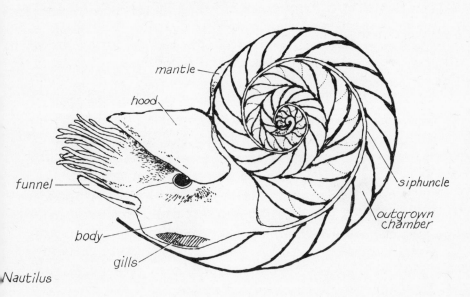

Nautilus

Group of Animals and Phylum Name	Class Name	Approximate No. of Kinds
CHORDATES [*Chordata*]		[45,000]
including mammals	Mammalia	15,000
birds	Aves	8,616
reptiles	Reptilia	4,000
amphibians	Amphibia	2,000
fishes, cartilaginous and bony	Pisces	15,000
cyclostomes	Cyclostomata	10
ECHINODERMS [*Echinodermata*]		[5,700]
including brittle stars	Ophiuroidea	
sea urchins	Echinoidea	
sea cucumbers	Holothuroidea	
sea stars	Asteroidea	
sea lilies	Crinoidea	
ARTHROPODS [*Arthropoda*]		[770,000]
including insects	Insecta	700,000
millipedes	Diplopoda	6,500
centipedes	Chilopoda	1,500
crustaceans	Crustacea	30,000
spiders and kin	Arachnida	33,000
horseshoe crabs	Merostomata	5
SEGMENTED WORMS [*Annelida*]		[7,000]
including leeches	Hirudinea	
earthworms and kin	Oligochaeta	
paddle-footed worms		
MOLLUSKS [*Mollusca*]		[100,00]
including cephalopods	Cephalopoda	400
clams and kin	Pelecypoda	25,000
snails and kin	Gastropoda	74,000
chitons	Amphineura	600
MOSS ANIMALS [*Bryozoa*]		4,000
WHEEL ANIMALCULES [*Rotifera*]		1,500
ROUNDWORMS [*Nematoda*]		10,500
FLATWORMS [*Platyhelminthes*]		[15,000]
including tapeworms	Cestoda	
flukes	Trematoda	
turbellarians	Turbellaria	
COELENTERATES [*Coelenterata*]		[9,600]
including corals and sea anemones	Anthozoa	
hydroids and medusae	Hydrozoa and Scyphozoa	
SPONGES [*Porifera*]		[4,500]
OTHER INVERTEBRATES WITH MANY CELLS		[2,000]
including arrowworms [*Chaetognatha*]		50
peripatuses [*Onychophora*]		70
spiny-headed worms [*Acanthocephala*]		400
ribbon worms [*Nemertea*]		570
comb-jellies [*Ctenophora*]		80
UNICELLULAR ANIMALS [*Protozoa*]		30,000

CHAPTER
2

Aquatic Animals

About four-fifths of the world's surface—some 140 million square miles—lies under the oceans, the home of more great groups of animals than any fresh waters or areas of exposed land. Anyone who visits the seashore knows what a wealth of life is tossed on the beach by every storm. Along rocky coasts, animals in even greater variety cling to the solid surfaces, and remain in pools exposed between the boulders when the tide is out.

A coating suggesting foam rubber, colored bright green or lemon-yellow or rose-pink, fastened to a rock usually turns out to be an encrusting sponge. In tropical waters a skin diver has to learn which ones to avoid, for some are "fire sponges" whose surfaces are studded with fine glass needles. They easily penetrate human skin and irritate like a burn. Most sponges have conspicuous holes in the surface, large enough to admit a wooden match or a pencil. From these openings, the loose community of cells expels water from branching central cavities. The water has been drawn into the sponge through pores too small to see with the unaided eye.

Sponges are more aware of their surroundings than one might guess. Dr. Maurice Burton of the British Museum found that, if the rock to which a sponge is attached is shifted, the colony is likely to break into fragments which move to new positions. Or the cells may rearrange themselves until the sponge is once more able to benefit from gravity and tidal currents. Sponges have no muscular or nervous system, and must depend entirely upon chemical messages to coordinate the separate cells. Yet the colony can respond as an individual.

Exposed rocks often bear tufts of feathery sea ferns, perhaps four or five inches long. Sea ferns are actually colonies of animals, related to the corals. Sometimes they are gathered, killed, dried, and dyed a bright green, then sold in novelty stores as a "house plant" that needs no watering. In warm oceans near shore, visitors are often shown sea fans waving in the current. These are like the sea ferns in bearing dozens or hundreds of tiny, globular individual animals, each extending its petal-like fringe of fleshy tentacles armed with special nettling cells that sting and cling to smaller animals as food. Each is a hydroid.

Sea anemones, living in groups or singly, have rubbery bodies that seem merely larger versions of the individual animals comprising sea fans and corals. Each sea anemone cements itself in place and stands like an artificial flower, snow-white or pink or tan or faintly green. If the fishing at high tide proves to be poor, the animal will free itself and gradually glide to a new position, although usually remaining where the full force of wave action does not strike it.

On both coasts of America, some sea anemones reach a length of 12 inches or more, and several inches in diameter. Large ones can subdue a fish six inches long. The poison from the anemone's nettling cells penetrates the victim's blood stream, ending its struggles quickly and letting the anemone engulf a dinner. The full process may take five minutes. No one who has watched it will ever again think of a sea anemone as anything but a hungry animal.

In crevices between the rocks, where crabs scuttle from one tide pool to another, bright metallic blue mussels commonly tether their bivalve shells. The tie cords are fine plastic threads secreted by the tongue-shaped foot. They hold the mollusk where sea water carrying food particles will be reliably available. Sometimes mussels tie themselves to one another, forming a "scalp" of shellfish over a beach or a sand bar, protecting the shore from erosion by wave action.

The English essayist Charles Lamb believed that a mussel, once anchored, was fixed for life. He wrote:

How much more dignified leisure hath a mussel, glued to his impassable rocky limit, two inches square! He hears the tide roll over him backwards and forwards . . . but knows better than to take an outside place a-top on't. He is the owl of the sea, Minerva's fish—the fish of wisdom.

Actually, a mussel can move about. If the animal becames dissatisfied at one location, it extends its foot to the limit in some direction and produces a new attachment strand. Letting go of all its old tethers, the mussel swings free. Again it moves along. In a few days it can crawl many inches, leaving behind it a little trail of single threads that mark its route.

Periwinkles and other little snails in spiral shells creep over the rocks and seaweeds, seeking food whether the tide is in or out. But limpets and abalones, with shallow cap-shaped shells, rarely move while exposed to air. When the tide covers them well, they hunt about for plant food of many kinds. Often they stand with one part of the broad foot holding a bit of seaweed in place while the mouth is used to scrape fragments away.

Usually each limpet has its own home area, as a particular place on a special rock to which it travels when not on a foraging expedition. There the limpet clings despite the shock of waves. On soft rock, the rim of the shell may wear a conspicuous groove from being struck repeatedly against the surface, showing how exactly the limpet returned to its chosen place year after year.

Permanent attachment is the way of life among oysters and barnacles. Oysters are bivalve mollusks, whereas barnacles are arthropods, related to crabs and shrimps. While very young, both of these types of shellfish swim actively in the ocean. Then each settles on some solid object.

Each oyster lies down on its left side and cements the left-hand valve of its two-part shell to the rock. When the tide covers it, the oyster gapes its shell just enough to allow entry and discharge of a water current bringing oxygen and particles of food. Hairlike cilia on the oyster's mantle (the fold of flesh lining the shell) create the current and drive the water through the gills while the animal lies in apparent indolence.

A young barnacle, upon attaching itself to a rock or a piling or a boat bottom or the firm skin of a whale, proceeds to shed its eyes or absorb them. At the same time it secretes a limy shell of several pieces, and closes doorlike parts against dry air when the tide is out. As soon as the sea

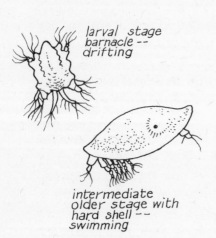

larval stage
barnacle --
drifting

intermediate
older stage with
hard shell --
swimming

Barnacle

mature barnacle--
permanently
anchored in place

covers the barnacle, the animal opens and reaches out with feathery feet to pull a current of food-laden water into its mouth. In Puget Sound, between Washington State and British Columbia, one kind of barnacle grows to a diameter of as much as 11 inches, and is useful as human food.

Tide pools often reveal familiar sea stars and spiny sea urchins clinging to the rocks by hundreds of soft tube-feet. Only members of the group to which these animals belong —the echinoderms—have tube-feet and the hydraulic system for extending them. Each tube-foot is hollow, muscular, and ends in a small suction cup under perfect control. Echinoderms use their tube-feet also for handling food and for cleaning the surface of the body.

Some sea urchins hold bits of seaweed or pebbles and pieces of coral over their bodies, shading themselves from sunlight in shallow water. Others quickly turn their long needle-sharp spines toward anything that shadows them, as though daring a fish to attack. A sea urchin's shell actually contains tasty food. Islanders in the West Indies eat urchins as "sea eggs." Gulls along New England coasts break open the urchins' shells by dropping them on rocks or highway pavement, then swoop down to enjoy the contents.

For many years, man has suspected that each plant and animal on land corresponds to one beneath the waves. His long list of sea eggs, sea ferns, water bugs, and water fleas bears this out. Aristotle followed this custom in the fourth century B.C. As he dissected a sea urchin, perhaps for the first time that this had been done with care, he saw that the five little white teeth coming together around the animal's mouth are part of a remarkable organ. Today we would compare it to a dredge, and realize that this is indeed its role. But Aristotle wrote that

The mouth-apparatus of the urchin is continuous from one end to the other, but to outward appearance it is not so, but looks like a horn lantern with the panes of horn left out.

The tooth-carrying organ has been known ever since as "Aristotle's lantern"—the lightless lantern of the sea.

Sea stars, often called starfishes, demonstrate how great a pull the tube-feet can exert in concert. These animals feed on bivalve mollusks, and fold their seemingly stiff bodies over a clam or a mussel while applying every tube-foot to one or the other half of the victim's shell. If the mollusk is strong and clamps its valves together, the sea star works even harder and actually bends the shell halves enough to open a crack between them. Through this slot the star extends its filmy stomach, and wraps it around the body of the clam. Soon the stomach's digestive action destroys the mollusk's ability to hold the shell together. It gapes, and the star completes its clam dinner with ease.

Animals of Sandy Shores and Muddy Bottoms

Sandy shores and muddy bottoms have their own types of life. If protected from the full force of storms, these coasts become fringed with the narrow-leaved flowering plants called eelgrass and turtlegrass. Among this vegetation the edible blue crab scavenges. And where the water is warm enough through the winter, little bay scallops swim about. These delightfully active clams, whose shell pattern has been taken for the trademark of a big oil company, gobble their way through the water by jet propulsion. They swim most actively when they detect the flavor of a sea star in their vicinity.

A person walking barefoot in the water along a sandy sea shore may feel the hard shell of a sand dollar or a heart urchin just below the surface. These burrowing echinoderms scavenge there for food. A hole large enough to admit a finger may be one end of a U-shaped tunnel built by a marine worm. Many of these animals remain in their tubes, capturing food particles and absorbing oxygen from water propelled through the passageway by rhythmic beating of the paddles on each body segment.

Along the Atlantic coast of America from Maine to Florida, and around the Gulf of Mexico as far as Yucatan, the sandy and muddy bottoms close to shore are the hunting grounds of an ancient style of animal known popularly as a horseshoe crab. *Limulus polyphemus* is not a crab at all, but a living relic of a kind of life that appeared on earth half a billion years ago. Its nearest surviving kin are scorpions and spiders.

Possibly the first description of a horseshoe crab and the earliest illustration of it were the work of Thomas Hariot and John White, the two naturalists who came to Virginia in 1584—85 with colonists sent from England by Sir Walter Raleigh. Hariot included in his list of the fish in the New World the statement that

The Seékanauk, a kind of crusty shellfish . . . about a foot wide, has a crusty tail, many legs, like a crab, and its eyes are set in its back. It can be found in salt water shallows or on the shore.

John White's water-color drawings, made on the spot, formed the basis for careful engravings published in 1590. The page showing the horseshoe crab mentions that

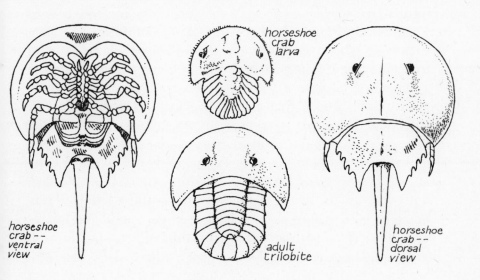

horseshoe
crab
larva

horseshoe
crab --
ventral
view

adult
trilobite

horseshoe
crab --
dorsal
view

They [the Indians] have a remarkable way of fishing in their rivers. As they have neither steel nor iron, they fasten the sharp, hollow tail of a certain fish (something like a sea crab) to reeds or to the end of a long rod, and with this point they spear fish, both by day and by night.

The Indians also ate horseshoe crabs. They often saved as charms the twisted little claws with which the bull crabs hold to the shells of the larger cow crabs. The female partner drags her mate with her until she is ready to lay her eggs.

The Reverend S. Lockwood gave a more appropriate name to the animal in 1870 when he called it the horsefoot crab and the "marine mole." The front portion of the creature's shell does suggest the form of a horse's hoof. It uses its body as a bulldozer while scrambling ponderously through surface mud in search of a mixed diet of seaweed, worms, young clams, and other forms of life. Only when the horseshoe crab swims does it show any graceful movements. Then its legs and the plates covering its leaflike gills beat rhythmically, propelling the body onward, upside down, like a coracle beneath the waves. Eventually the swimmer settles to the bottom on its back, and uses its long tail spine to expertly right itself.

At extreme low tide, many mudflats continue to bubble with little jets of sea water expelled by buried clams. Among them may be quahogs, which the Indians of New England appreciated both as a food and as a source of shell money (wampum). Today this animal provides an annual harvest valued at hundreds of thousands of dollars, to reach the hungry public in the form of fried clams or clams steamed and dipped in melted butter. For novelty and perhaps taste as well, this burrower of the Atlantic coast is excelled, however, by the giant clam known as the geoduck (pronounced goo'-ee-duck) which lives in Puget Sound and Pacific beaches as far south as northern California.

The digging of geoducks is a sport, with a daily bag limit

of three. So huge is this monster clam that its seven-inch shell valves no longer close around it. Instead, the thick and tender mantle protrudes and has become famous as the animal's "breast" meat. Still, the geoduck has a sporting chance. Full-grown ones may be four feet down in the soft mud and, at the touch of a shovel to the beach (or even an incautious footstep), they pull in the long neck that previously reached up to open water. Digging three clams from this depth before the tide returns requires both brawn and engineering skill.

Drifting and Swimming Sea Animals

A beachcomber on the watch for clams may find a jellyfish cast ashore, or notice one pulsating in the water beside a pier or boat. If the jellyfish is a golden bell rather than a colorless or blue individual, he is wise to keep his distance. Golden jellies often prove to be the kind called the lion's mane, with an especially virulent poison in its nettling cells. Or if a bather by the shore sees a fleet of iridescent blue floats drifting toward the beach, he had better stay on land. Each float is the bulbous sail of a Portuguese man-of-war, below and behind which dark blue tentacles may trail as much as 40 feet, armed with a violent poison.

But most animals met along the shore are harmless. They provide an intriguing sample of the myriad kinds that inhabit the vast realms of the sea. Yet modern knowledge of ocean animals remains superficial. It is one thing to measure the distance to the bottom and learn that the average depth of the oceans is 12,451 feet. It is quite another to catch creatures living far down. In consequence, some of the planet's least known animals live out their days barely more than 300 yards below the crowded steamer lanes on the world's oceans. Their privacy is without equal, for it is enforced by the weight of water above them. Man has ventured into their realm, bobbing at the end of a steel cable in an armored bathysphere, or peering from the windows of a special submarine, the bathyscaphe. But routine explorations (a requirement for real familiarity with animals of the depths) may be harder to manage than human excursions on the surface of the moon.

All of the sun's energy is absorbed in the upper levels of the ocean. Only in the topmost 600 feet can green plants carry on their essential photosynthesis. Here is the "pasture of the sea," richest where the great currents cause upwelling of cold bottom water charged with mineral nutrients. Rich parts of the pasture are the fishing banks for man, and a magnet for sea birds of many kinds.

Perhaps 90 per cent of the minute plants are eaten by seed-sized crustaceans and small fishes such as anchovies and young herrings, which have special filters between their gills, helping them to strain out the algal cells. The crustaceans and small fishes, in turn, are food for larger fishes that feed near the surface, and for sea birds such as auks, cormorants, gannets, murres, and puffins.

So long as ocean currents bring to the surface water from the bottom, carrying along mineral nutrients of many kinds, the miscroscopic plants prosper and so do the fishermen. Along the coast of Peru, conditions of this kind favor the white-fronted cormorants known as guanay birds. The excrement from these birds on offshore islands, where they nest, has accumulated in places to a depth of 150 feet. Peruvians mine the guano for shipment as fertilizer all over the world.

Occasionally, some vagary of weather alters the pattern of water currents in the Pacific Ocean along the Peruvian coast, and the upwelling of nutrients from the deeps ceases. The cold northbound coastal current may be replaced by southbound warm water from the Gulf of Panama. The microscopic algae decline. The crustaceans and filter-feeding fishes starve or move to greater depths to get other food. Neither the fishermen nor the guanay birds can find the fish they need.

Warm currents off the Peruvian coast may bring on a season of rains on the normally arid shores. Rivers come tumbling to the sea with sediments that stimulate the growth of very different microscopic life in surface waters. Some of these creatures, the armored dinoflagellates, reproduce so rapidly that they use up all of the available oxygen each night. Sea animals suffocate by the thousands and are washed ashore. Fishermen recognize the red color the dinoflagellates give the water. "Red tides," they complain, "are killing all our fish."

In many parts of the open sea, a majority of the small crustaceans feed on the drifting green plants in surface waters only at night. With the approach of dawn, the crustaceans swim downward, following the black edge of twilight into the sea. After spending the sunny hours between 500 and 1,200 feet below the surface, they start up again in late afternoon. Because the lower, dark waters rarely travel in the same direction or at the same speed as the surface layers, these animals dive from one mass or "algal pasture" and rise to feed in a different one. This prevents the crustaceans from interfering seriously with the reproduction of the drifting algae.

Fishes that feed on small crustaceans may follow down and up each day. Squids that pursue the fishes go along. Seals that catch the squids must dive for them, and so do the toothed whales such as the killer and the cachalot. Whalebone whales, among which the great blue and the humpback are most famous, plow through the upper levels of the sea, filtering out the crustaceans and the smallest fishes. They feed most successfully at night when the surface waters are so much more thickly populated.

Animals of the Abysses

At depths between 600 and 3,000 feet below the surface, from two-thirds to four-fifths of the marine fishes carry their own lights with them. In the same dark water, luminous spots mark squids and prawns and the shrimplike crustaceans known as krill. Some of the prawns add to the underwater display an occasional burst of luminous fluid which remains, like a brilliant cloud, after its maker has darted off.

No doubt most of these bright markings provide a means of recognition in the dark. Some are used only when several individuals of a single kind are swimming together; the spots are running lights that help keep the animals in formation. Others enable the sexes to identify one another. Still others are clearly lures for prey. Angler fishes are grotesque creatures with a luminous knob on the end of a projection like a fishing pole and line. They dangle the bright tip just in front of their huge mouths, and gulp in any victim that nibbles at the bait. Some of the dragonfishes swim slowly with their mouths widely open, displaying the luminous roof of the cavity, then snap shut on reckless creatures that investigate.

Between 600 feet and the great abysses, the hues of animals often match their dietary habits. Those that sweep through the dark water with open mouths as the "nighthawks of the deep" are usually silvered like a mirror; they strain from their surroundings any small particles of food that come their way. Swimmers that prey upon seed-sized crustaceans, taking them one at a time, tend to be red-flecked pink, or gray. But the fishes that wait and watch, ready to pounce on neighbors who pass too close, usually wear a complete suit of black with no reflections or paler ornaments of any kind.

Below 600 feet, the animals must depend for food upon the crustaceans fleeing from daylight, upon the fishes and

Angler fish
with
luminous
lure

squids that follow the crustaceans, and upon the corpses that sink from the upper levels as a sort of manna. So chancy is this source of nourishment that many of the deep-sea creatures are fitted to take advantage of outsized opportunities. A slender, eight-inch blackdragon fish can unfold its jaws to swallow a victim whose body is twice as great in diameter. In accomplishing this feat, the blackdragon swings wide its gills, like garage doors, and takes full advantage of the position of its heart, far forward under the chin where it does not conflict for space with the stomach. A three-inch fangtooth fish, although only half grown, could accommodate a golf ball in its cavernous mouth, behind jaws rimmed with a murderous array of daggerlike teeth.

The abysses are home to some of the world's most amazing fishes, such as the blacksmelts—possessors of the largest eyes in proportion to body size of any vertebrate animal—and the bigscales, whose name fails to show "How big?" The blacksmelt comes so nearly to being all eyes that its visual organs often occupy a third of the area of its broad, blunt head. And on an individual bigscale fish less than four inches long, a single scale may be ¾ of an inch across. A bigscale has correspondingly fewer pieces in its armor. Any beachcombers who treasure a tarpon scale as a giant should realize that, to equal a bigscale, a six-foot tarpon would have to have scales 13½ inches across—not just three or four.

Animals freshly hauled from great depths are usually still very cold. We remember one particular netful from 4,200 feet below the surface, collected in spring aboard the research vessel *Stranger*. Nearly 10,000 specimens came up from the dark waters; they retained much of the chill of their home level, where the temperature stood at 38 degrees Fahrenheit—30 degrees cooler than at the surface. Around them at this depth had been a pressure of more than a ton to the square inch, turning the water into a sort of syrup with twice the viscosity of the free-running liquid everyone knows.

Of the nearly 10,000 animals, about 4 per cent were fishes. Few of them reached two inches in length, and only five fishes exceeded six inches. Bulkiest of the catch were deep-sea jellyfishes and soft-bodied squids. The two largest specimens were squids, each eight inches long and literally pint-sized. Like so many creatures living under enormous pressures, their bodies felt heavy and gelatinous. To transfer one from the pail to a tray, we had to cradle it gently in two hands so that it would not tear apart through its own weight.

These two squids were particular prizes, for few of them have been recovered in good condition. Professor Carl Chun, who led the German Deep-sea Expedition at the end of the last century, was the first to meet these blackish purple animals. He gave them the imaginative name *Vampyroteuthis infernalis*—the "vampire squid of the infernal regions." The vampire squid bears suction cups on only eight of its ten arms, but these eight are linked to one another by a web suggesting the fabric of a parachute. Perhaps the web lets the creature sink slowly whenever it stops swimming. The remaining two arms are mere slender feelers, kept hidden in special pockets.

Since no one has seen the vampire squid in its native haunts between 3,600 and 8,200 feet below the surface, we hurried our one surviving individual into the darkroom—water, tray, and all. In a few minutes our eyes grew sensitive enough to let us see a pair of elaborate glowing knobs as thick as a man's forefinger. They had popped out of slits near the blunt rear of the body, and in the light had been brilliant as silvery reflectors. Two clusters of luminous spots shone on what corresponded to the back of the animal's neck. Twinkling stars covered the whole body except for the inner surface of the web linking the eight arms. The vampire squid may use the unrelieved blackness of this area around its mouth as a cloak behind which to disappear from enemies, or while approaching some wary fish glowing in the depths.

Ever since 1873, when the science of oceanography was

born with the famous voyage of H.M.S. *Challenger*, nets and dredges have been sent down on weighted lines, towed at known rates for definite lengths of time at predictable depths, and hauled up full of astonishing animals. But until 1957, none of the deep-sea creatures collected in this way proved to be a real "missing link," completely unlike anything found near the surface. The special surprise was discovered among an assortment hauled aboard the Danish research vessel *Galathea* from 11,760 feet down in the Pacific Ocean off the coast of Nicaragua. It was a limpetlike mollusk whose soft body showed features never before seen in this great group of animals, features linking mollusks to the segmented worms. The shell of the newly found animal corresponded to types known only among the earliest of fossils—a group of shellfish previously believed extinct for at least 500 million years. The missing link was given the name *Neopilina galatheae,* in honor of the expedition ship.

Otherwise the animals of the great abysses have been near-relatives of kinds encountered close to shore. Apparently, millions of years ago, they spread downward away from daylight, perhaps at about the same time that other sea creatures invaded fresh waters.

At first glance, a person might wonder why an animal would need to leave the sea, unless to escape overcrowding. But oxygen is more available from air, and green plants grow where daylight reaches them. Shallower water may be fresh. Land offers these opportunities, too. Animals that could do so have spread into these other realms, even though their ancestors all lived in the sea.

For the most part, the animals found in today's oceans are those that adjusted progressively to increased salt. Animals that become independent of the sea's salt not only established a blood concentration they could maintain indefinitely, but they also moved into estuaries, up rivers and, in many cases, to land. Careful experiments support the idea that an egg has a slightly better chance of surviving in water less salty than modern oceans. This may be the decisive factor that leads horseshoe crabs and such fishes as grunions and caplins to spawn in the beach at high tide, and brings the sea turtles ashore each spring. Rain water may be the factor that helps their embryos grow.

Animals of Fresh Water

The earth has only about a million square miles of fresh waters, and they afford far fewer advantages than the sea. They are subject to flood and drought, to rushing currents and to dismal stagnation. In summer the surface waters of a lake and its drainage stream may become too warm for game fish. At the same time the cold depths of the lake contain so little oxygen that for ordinary animals respiration becomes impossible. In water a pond may freeze to the bottom, or a lake come to be roofed with ice so thick that the exchange of carbon dioxide for oxygen from the atmosphere is blocked. And merely in being fresh, a river or a lake contains so few dissolved substances that an animal must have special abilities to absorb the amounts it needs. To many an ocean dweller, fresh water is too pure to tolerate even briefly.

Despite these disadvantages, a great many kinds of animals do live in fresh water. Apparently their ancestors began laying eggs in the brackish estuaries, or even living there. With no planning, these regions of lower and varying salinity served as staging areas for a later assault upon the flowing rivers.

The difference between sea water and fresh is not great. Ocean water is 96½ per cent water and 3½ per cent salts dissolved in it. To be classed as "fresh," a lake or river must be at least 99½ per cent water. The salt concentration of human blood falls between the two, a fact that becomes important in emergencies when no blood plasma or whole blood is available to a person who has bled severely; a solution of table salt—99$\frac{1}{10}$ per cent water and $\frac{9}{10}$ of one per cent salt—can be injected to bolster the volume of liquid passing through the pumping heart and stave off shock. Yet no man can continue to drink sea water—four times as salty as his blood—without serious consequences. Neither can many fish. Only a very few migrate back and forth, spending part of their lives in the oceans. The rest find the slight difference between the sea and fresh water a barrier they cannot cross.

In the distant past, the sea's lesser salinity must have made the barrier between oceans and rivers less obvious. Some flatworms crossed the hurdle; today their descendents in fresh water are the scavenging turbellarians. They creep over stones in the riffles, so close to the rock surface that the current barely brushes them. And in the speed with which they collect on a piece of meat tied in the stream can be seen their importance in keeping the river clean.

Ponds and streams are home to many mollusks. For years, in fact, the pearl button industry of America depended upon clams collected for their shells in the various branches of the slow-flowing Mississippi River.

These freshwater clams have a way to distribute their young without much danger of the current carrying the offspring to the sea. Unlike clams in the ocean, the river clams do not broadcast their eggs. Instead, each female uses her capacious gills as a brood sac. The eggs she lays into her gills remain there until the little embryos have grown special paired shells armed with tonglike hooks. They are larvae (glochidia), scarcely resembling the parent.

As the larvae become ready, the mother clam flushes them out a few at a time, day after day, usually when the sun is shining brightly. The intermittent stream of young is visible in the shallows as a series of particles reflecting the light. Fishes are attracted and snap up the larval clams, only to have them lodge in the gills and become parasites there. Or the clam larvae sink their hooks into the skin of a passing fish, and soon begin to absorb a minute meal of blood.

Probably any healthy fish can carry dozens of larval clams without suffering. By the time the hitchhikers have grown and taken adult form and dropped to the bottom, they are usually far from the mother clam. Yet, because the fishes do not stray from fresh water, the little clams are distributed into other parts of the same river system.

For mollusks to steal a ride on fish and even take from them a little blood is an instance of turnabout, since many fish depend for food largely upon mollusks. Freshwater snails are a particular prey, and gain their greatest protection by creeping among the tangled vegetation of a marsh. There, of course, they may be found by herons and other birds. The cranelike limpkin of the Okefenokee Swamp and the Florida Everglades eats almost nothing else.

The segmented worms in fresh water both gain and lose from their vertebrate neighbors. The slender, cylindrical relatives of earthworms found in the bottom mud of ponds, slow streams, and lakes are hunted out by many kinds of fish and turtles. But the flattened leeches, with their anchoring suckers front and rear, take every opportunity to space out meals on small crustaceans with blood sucked from a fish or a turtle. The famous medicinal leech of Europe is raised in freshwater ponds, often as a by-product of carp culture.

Both leeches and fishes would be harder pressed for food if a wide assortment of crustaceans had not found fresh waters to their liking. The crayfishes of streams and rivers are the counterparts of lobsters in the sea. Prawns in tropic brooks are scarcely different from their ocean-going relatives. The little flattened scuds of ponds suggest diminutive shrimps. And a host of water fleas browse on the drifting microscopic algae of lakes and slow rivers, corresponding to the seed-sized crustaceans in the sea.

Springtime, ponds, and the songs of frogs and toads all go together, for the fresh waters are home to virtually all of the world's amphibians. They return regularly to lay their eggs, and spend at least their younger swimming stages in ponds or swamps or sluggish streams. Each of us as a child

has met the black, round-bodied, legless tadpoles and has
delighted in watching the transformation of tadpole into frog
or toad. Fewer people discover the graceful, four-legged
slender young of newts and salamanders in a pond or marsh.
Unlike the vegetarian tadpoles, the little salamanders pursue
worms and small arthropods, stalking each victim with extreme care or swimming after it by an undulation of body
and tail.

Scarlet water mites and a good many kinds of insects live
in fresh waters. Nowhere else can a mayfly raise its young.
Or a dragonfly. Or a damselfly. Or a stonefly. Or a hellgra-
mite. The water bugs are all *fresh*water bugs. So are the
water boatmen. The backswimmers and the diving beetles
perform their acrobatics only in fresh water. It is there that
the caddisworms build their snares and cases. Fresh water
provides also the nursery in which mosquitoes and blackflies
raise their young.

The world's lakes, rivers, marshes, and swamps are rich
in animal inhabitants. But something more can be read into
the roster of great groups that succeed in establishing themselves firmly there. The types that conquered fresh water are
also those which invaded the land. Rivers and lakes have
served as liquid avenues from the sea to terrestrial life.

Seemingly this route was closed to comb jellies, to arrow-
worms, to chitons and cephalopods among the mollusks, to
paddle-footed worms, and to all of the echinoderms. These
are found neither in fresh water nor on land.

A few dozen kinds of freshwater sponges and a scattering
of moss animals (bryozoans) represent these two groups
from the sea. When they spread into conduits for water supplies, sanitary engineers refer to them both as "pipe moss,"
and scarcely know that two very different types of life are
being lumped together. Freshwater sponges are often green
with congenial algae growing through them; these incrusta-
tions and coatings on sunken logs or branches may be conspicuous in clear running water where the sun reaches the
bottom.

Moss animals build colonies like fine leafless vines, or form gelatinous masses on immersed parts of boat docks and underwater wood. None of these creatures ever become terrestrial; their freshwater outposts are only token representation of kinds of flourishing in the sea.

Both the sponges and moss animals of fresh waters have solved in comparable ways the problems of drought and winter weather. Toward autumn or when a stream shrinks into a series of isolated ponds, the sponges and moss animals produce little clusters of cold-resistant cells and surround them with a moisture-proof covering. The parent colony can die and disintegrate, but the protected reproductive bodies remain. They may wait until springtime when warmer waters are suitable for new growth. Or they may become dry particles, blown by the wind or carried on the muddy feet of birds to new locations.

The great group of the coelenterates is barely represented in fresh waters; most members are marine. One kind of freshwater jellyfish is almost cosmopolitan. Its fertilized eggs develop into minute sedentary creatures, each resembling a solitary coral animal or the little hydras that live in the same locations. From the attached individuals, new jellyfishes are released, completing the life cycle.

The first freshwater jellies ever known to science were found in a tank of water lilies under the glass-covered dome of a greenhouse in England's famous Kew Gardens. The same kind of jellyfishes have appeared suddenly in swimming pools and artificial lakes on almost every continent. They are suspected of developing from the minute attached stage, which somehow get airlifted from pond to pond on the muddy feet of a wading bird, or transferred unnoticed on some water plants.

Probably freshwater hydras travel in the same way. They are among the most indestructable of animals. A hydra can be chopped into pieces, and each part will become a whole new individual, attached to a water weed or suspended below a lily pad by one end of the cylindrical body. From the opposite end, six or eight long slender tentacles reach out for minute animals as prey, to be captured and pushed whole into the mouth amid the tentacles.

The adults of water insects fly from pond to pond. Even a bird bath is big enough to attract them. The British entomologist, Dr. T. T. Macan, recorded a regular sequence of aquatic insects as they came by air to the reflecting pool around a new ornamental fountain. First to arrive were water boatmen (corixids), little bugs that row along beneath the surface. Backswimmers (notonectid bugs) followed, soon to be joined by diving beetles and others.

A naturalist who notices water plants and animals of insect size can feel amazingly at home anywhere in the world, if he gets in a rowboat and sculls his way over a fresh pond or stream. The water-lily pads and the insects on them are much the same, whether in the Arctic or the Tropics. The shores in the one instance may be home to moose and polar bear, in the other to sloths and monkeys. But on the water surface of almost any quiet bay or stream, flotillas of jet-black whirligig beetles will zig and zag like diminutive speed-boats in a motion picture running far too fast. Familiar water striders will police the surface film, and dragonflies hawk for gnats in the air above. Their immature stages will be there, too, those of the dragonflies stalking each other or little worms and crustaceans on the bottom. The river or lake or pond will be alive with case-building caddisworms, and scarlet water mites, and the naiads of mayflies. Each stone in a stream will shelter a host of the same types of animals, no matter what part of the world surrounds it.

Animals of the Water Film

Most paradoxical of all the aquatic animals are those that walk on water without getting wet. Suspended between the air above and the depths below, they inhabit an almost two-dimensional realm—the surface film of ponds, streams, lakes, and even oceans. They seem to contradict all human experience as they rest or scamper along, demonstrating that to them the water has a skin, elastic and smooth, stretching from shore to shore.

No walkers on the water are known more universally than the water striders. Some people call them "water skippers." In Canada they are "skaters" and in Texas, "Jesus bugs." Four long legs, scarcely thicker than a horsehair, spread to the sides and rest upon the water film. Hair-booted feet present waxy surfaces to the water and repel it. The surface film sags below each outstretched foot, making an oval dimple that distorts the sunshine and may produce strange patterns on the bottom of the pond. On a sunny day, these bright-circled shadows are often more conspicuous than the slender insect making them, yet they drift along and follow every movement of the strider rowing on the film above.

The insect's weight is supported partly by the surface tension that tends to erase the depressions and bring all of the water film to the same level, and partly by the buoyant force of the water displaced from the dimples. So secure is the insect on a quiet pond that it can shift its weight freely among its feet to clean a leg or scratch its back or manipulate a bit of food. Even when it dashes across to investigate some object that has dropped into the water—leaf, petal, or juicy ant or fly—its fast-moving feet do not press through the surface film.

Occasionally a water strider is carried by the current over a dam or through a riffle and is plunged beneath the surface. Usually air clings to hairs on its body, keeping it just below the water film. The insect then rows along, reaching shore or a stone upon which it can crawl out and dry itself. A breeze that ruffles the water or a pelt of rain may also counteract the strider's seemingly magic ability to walk dryshod. At the first hint of either, most striders head for the bank, ready to leave the water and hide under a leaf until the weather improves. It is there that they spend the winter, too.

Among the mangrove swamps of tropical coasts, a seagoing water strider is much at home. These same insects are found far from land, riding the waves like the best sailors. No one knows what they do during a storm at sea, or when it rains there. They must get wet. How do they get dry again? To make the mystery deeper, in calm weather these marine striders often manage to go below the surface and row along, feeding on particles that have floated up from the depths. Hundreds of miles from shore they raise their families, laying their eggs on seaweed at the surface or on feathers dropped by passing birds.

A good many other insects alight on the water film and take off again as though it were a dry landing field. Small gnats and midges flit from place to place, settling on pond or lily pad with equal equanimity. Even large craneflies settle gracefully on the water's skin. Leafhoppers jump over the surface, using leaping legs comparable to those of a locust or cricket. They catapult themselves, getting airborne like a torpedo plane from a carrier's deck.

Wingless insects use the water film as a pasture and a playground. Springtails flip themselves over lakes and ponds. One type is so abundant that congregations of bluish black individuals sometimes create a conspicuous band several inches wide along the water's edge. Each walks among its fellows, but at the slightest disturbance, the whole group tosses itself into the air like tiny corn kernels popping on a hot griddle. The springtails fall back to the surface many inches away, no longer in groups. To all appearances they have vanished.

A springtail is a grotesque insect. It keeps its elongated tail curved under the body, between the six short legs, and almost resting on the water film. To jump, the animal merely straightens out. The tail whacks the surface, producing a momentary dimple, as the springtail flicks itself into the air. Yet for so small an insect, the air has a cushioning effect, letting the leaper settle again without damage and without danger of plunging into the pond.

Many springtails have a stubby projection from the underside of the body, by means of which they can hold themselves to the water film. A secretion from the projection's tip makes the water wetter, by reducing its surface tension. This gives the springtail a sort of anchor—one it can release upon a moment's notice.

Another animal seen upon the water film is able to reduce the surface tension deliberately and benefit. The little rove beetle *Stenus*, which runs and flies actively in search of carrion or small prey, sometimes drops into a puddle or a pond. It has no waxy hairs to keep its feet dry, and sinks in—getting legs and underparts thoroughly wetted by the water. But at the rear of its body, *Stenus* also carries glands producing a substance making water wetter. Undiminished surface forces in front of the beetle promptly draw it forward. So long as the insect continues to discharge this magical secretion, it sails along with no apparent effort. Eventually it may reach some dry object upon which it can crawl and ready itself for flight again.

For other insects the water film can be a barrier or a trap, depending on how they approach it. A heavy-bodied moth that blunders into a pond is almost sure to drown. But a dragonfly or caddisfly or mayfly ready to place an egg below the water surface may skim along in horizontal flight and flick the extruded egg through the film by a sudden downward thrust of the body tip. The insect's momentum carries it onward and withdraws the immersed portion of the abdomen without special effort.

The ordinary biting mosquitoes rest on the water film while depositing a whole raft of cigar-shaped eggs, each vertical against its neighbors. The bottom end of the raft is wetted by the water, and through it each egg hatches. Thereafter the young wriggler, being heavier than water, gets its atmospheric air by writhing and tossing itself to the surface and thrusting through the film a special breathing tube. For a minute or more at a time, the wriggler hangs suspended from the surface film while taking in the air it needs.

Mosquito-control officers learn that the dreaded carrier of malaria (*Anopheles*) lays her eggs singly, and the wrigglers differ in lying parallel to the water film while breathing. When the *Anopheles* wriggler goes into the pupal stage, however, it resembles the "bullhead" of less dangerous mosquitoes in being lighter than water. All bullheads must swim to descend into a pond. As soon as they stop jerking their tails, they float to the surface and press through the film a pair of little tubes like soda straws—snorkels through which they get air. And when the mosquito is ready to emerge, the bullhead skin provides a raft through which the adult insect can escape, avoiding all surface difficulties.

Water-lily pads provide floating airfields for many insects that are unable to alight on the surface film and escape again. One type of beetle regularly takes advantage of the fact that each pad has one dry surface and one wet. The beetle cuts a small circular hole through the lily leaf, pushes its abdominal tip through the opening into the water below, and lays two rows of eggs on the under side of the pad while standing high and dry on a firm support.

Fragile, fluttering damselflies cooperate in laying eggs below the water surface, where the young can emerge easily into the correct environment. With a pair of claspers at the end of his long abdomen, the male damselfly holds his mate by her slender neck. When her eggs are ready for laying, she somehow signals to him. The two alight on a reed growing out of the water. A step at a time she backs down below the surface, her gauzy wings trapping a bubble of air against her body. Her mate follows down the stem as far as he can go without wetting his own wings, and holds her neck securely. After her task is done, she starts upward and he pulls her through the surface, fluttering to exert extra force. This cooperation saves her life, and permits her to deposit eggs at a series of places along pond or stream.

Sometimes a female damselfly insists on backing deeper into the water, placing her eggs farther below the surface. Seldom can she induce her mate to take the extra step. Instead, he will release his hold upon her neck. If she does not take too long, he may remain waiting, ready to grasp her neck again and assist her from the water. But her independence is risky. If another female damselfly comes along while the first one is busy under water, the waiting male may flit off for a new conquest, leaving his earlier mate to drown.

More powerful insects, such as the largest caddisflies, wrap their wings about them like a cloak and stride down into the water to lay their eggs, perhaps hanging a doughnut-shaped ring of them in jelly over a submerged branch. Then upward through the surface film the insect shoulders its way, to dry off and fly again.

The Smaller Diving Animals

Many adult insects living in the water still depend upon atmospheric air, and employ a variety of methods in replenishing their supply for respiration. Diving beetles come to the surface at intervals, and use the tips of their water-repellent wing covers to push through the barrier film. With a big bubble imprisoned between abdomen and wing covers they dart below again, searching for the worms and tadpoles and little fishes that form their food. The water scorpions and giant water bugs (once known as "electric-light bugs" because of their frequent visits to early arc lamps used for street illumination) float head down at the surface while thrusting into air a pair of slender tail filaments. Through these, held together as a tube, a large air bubble is drawn under the overlapping wings.

Naturalists are often surprised to see these insects return to the surface for more air while the shiny bulge of the previous bubble still shows at the end of the body. Now the reason is known and, like so many scientific explanations, the principle seems obvious once it is understood. The oxygen and nitrogen dissolved in pond water are in equilibrium with the oxygen and nitrogen in the air above. The air bubble captured by the insect and held under its wings soon becomes poorer in oxygen as the insect breathes. Oxygen from the water comes out of solution into the bubble, replenishing the insect's supply. By keeping its bubble exposed to the water and hence visible, the insect continues to gain oxygen from the pond. At the same time, the bubble is richer in nitrogen than is the air over the pond. Consequently the nitrogen from the bubble slowly dissolves into the water. The insect trips to the surface when its nitrogen bubble becomes too small to hold exposed easily.

Spiders often carry air with them into a pond, as a silvery film over the animal's hairy body. The wolf spider *Dolomedes,* one of the largest to scamper over the surface of ponds and snatch insects on its way, walks down a partly submerged tree branch and clings there, waiting. If a small fish comes by, *Dolomedes* may snatch it and hurry back into the air with its prize. This spider's outstretched legs often straddle an area more than three inches in diameter. Sometimes its victim is a stickleback fish two inches long.

In Europe, an unrelated water spider descends into fresh water and builds a dome-shaped nest of closely woven silk between the stems of water weeds. The water spider then makes repeated trips between surface and nest, each time bringing down a load of air. When safely under the dome, the animal uses some of its legs to comb the air free from its body. The bubbles rise into the silken tent and are trapped there. In this way the water spider spins its own fixed diving bell and charges it with air. Oxygen from the pond keeps the big bubble of captive gas useful in respiration, and the spider is able to stay close to the fish and water insects it stalks.

The Larger Diving Animals

Despite its surface film as a barrier between the wet world and the dry, fresh water is more like land as a living space for animals than any part of the sea has ever been. So many terrestrial animals spend part of their lives in fresh water and so many aquatic animals make extended visits on land that a distinction between the two is sometimes almost meaningless. If a duck is terrestrial because it lays its eggs on land

and breaths air, so is a sea turtle that comes ashore only to hide its eggs in the beach. If a newt is aquatic because it lays its eggs in water, so is a toad in the desert, although years may pass before a succession of temporary ponds let its tadpoles reach the hopping stage.

Except that the larger air-breathing animals must visit the surface at intervals to refill their lungs, many of them seem as much at home in the water as any fish. Porpoises resemble their nearest relatives, the toothed whales, in being able to live only in water; they dive for food almost exclusively in the open sea. Seals, sea lions, and the walrus of arctic coasts are slightly more versatile, for they haul themselves out on shore for sunbaths or to give birth.

In fresh water, mink and muskrat are expert swimmers, diving for fish and crayfish, tadpole and salamander. They match the vegetarian beavers in an ability to hold their breath for long periods while searching for food under water or while escaping from danger by swimming for great distances below the surface.

Water birds, as distinguished by bird watchers from land birds, include the flightless penguins, which use their wings in swimming under water in pursuit of fish; the loons, gannets, pelicans, and other fish-eating birds that dive for their

Adélie penguin

dinners; the pink flamingos which wade about, filtering small creatures as food from the shallow water; the herons and cranes which rarely swim, but frequent the marshes where frogs and small fish can be caught; as well as a great variety of ducks and geese and gulls, some of which regularly walk about on land, grazing on fresh vegetation or expertly catching insects. No really strict line can be drawn between animals of the water and of the land.

Even the fishes—the most completely aquatic of the larger animals—come out of their element upon occasion. Trout burst into air in pursuit of insects. Salmon leap freely while hurdling low waterfalls. The archer fish of the Amazon slowly thrusts its head out of the stream and spouts a well-aimed jet of water to knock food from overhanging branches. Ten-inch flying fishes take to the air for 500-foot glides while dodging larger fishes pursuing them from below the surface or when frightened by an approaching ship. Nor do most fishes dive as deeply as the mammals that pursue them. A few hundred feet vertically appears to change the pressure more than a fish finds comfortable, whereas air-breathing whales have become entangled in transoceanic telephone cables lying on the bottom, thousands of feet below the surface.

C H A P T E R

3

Land Animals

More than four-fifths of all the different kinds of animals in the world live on land, although this is a mere one-fifth of the planet's surface. For them, home may be anywhere from the water's edge to the top of a lofty mountain, and from the Equator almost to the poles. The Arctic teems with animal life, whereas the tropical jungle while appearing deserted conceals an immense variety. Even the most arid lands, where dew and rain and snow are rarities, have been colonized by a few special kinds of creatures.

Of all the substances that animals require for activity, only one is more abundant to terrestrial life than to creatures below the surface of water. Oxygen, so necessary for continued muscular activity, is one part in every five of the atmosphere. By contrast, the seas and fresh waters never contain more than one part in every 14,500. In water, an animal must find a natural current or create an artificial one to bring it more oxygen in solution. In air, the gases intermingle so freely that no animal in the open needs a breeze or some fanning action to bring it more oxygen.

Air offers its oxygen as reliably when warm as when cold. By contrast, water holds in solution less and less oxygen as the temperature rises. At the temperature of human blood, which is ideal for the chemical processes upon which most kinds of life depend, water holds no more than one part of oxygen in every 31,200. Generally this is too little for aquatic animals that rely on gills for breathing. In air, animals survive high temperatures that would be fatal to them in a water environment.

The land is called *terra firma* with good reason. Even during a storm, a terrestrial animal can crouch in some sheltered corner and let the wind go by. Dust and debris driven by a tornado on land may make life difficult briefly. But under similar circumstances, animals in water tend to dive deep and stay below. Sediments may bury them permanently. Near the surface, however, they are battered by great waves produced by storms of just ordinary proportions.

The greater availability of oxygen and the solidarity of land are advantages that must be paid for. A terrestrial animal must support its body, without the assistance of water's buoyancy. It has to survive sudden changes in temperature, and may suffer from sudden heat or cold. The temperature of air changes four times as rapidly as that of water when the same amount of heat energy is added or withdrawn. Moreover, for much of the day and year, the passing breeze can steal an animal's body moisture—water it must retain if it is to survive.

Desiccation is often the greatest hazard a land animal faces. To avoid this danger, an immense number of different creatures live only in steamy jungles. Some of them emerge from hiding and are active only at night or after a prolonged rain has coated virtually everything with a film of moisture. At such times even the tops of the highest trees are accessible to animals lacking real protection against drying out. Jungle planarians (turbellarians) glide about freely in the rainy season. One of these flatworms, *Bipalium kewense*, has now adopted as a substitute for the dank forests the greenhouses in which man raises orchids and other tropical vegetation.

High humidity is essential to a slug. The thin coating of clear mucus over its body cannot shield it for more than a few minutes against dry air or sun. Most slugs carry a generous supply of a milk-white secretion, valuable in repelling attackers. If a bird takes an experimental peck at one of these mollusks while it is still active after dawn, the injured slug may squirt out jets of slime like a fireboat celebrating the arrival of some dignitary. If the bird is struck by any of the secretion, it usually hurries off to preen itself clean, and thereafter lets slugs alone.

In its spiral shell, a land snail can wait for many months if necessary, until humid weather comes along. In this way these creatures have been able to colonize the deserts, sometimes continuing inactive for two or three years if no rain chances to fall. Even the slightly lessened humidity of a Florida winter is enough to induce the handsomely banded tree snails (*Liguus*) of the Everglades and Keys to cement their shell rim to a tree trunk and retire into dormancy.

Burrowers in the Soil

A majority of the land animals that can suspend activity spend their dormant weeks in the soil. Most land snails follow this pattern. So, in a sense, do ants. Through winter and other inclement weather, they remain in their underground galleries. Strong sun, too, may send them home. But in the more humid parts of the day, the workers emerge on foraging expeditions.

While the sun is high and warm, nurse ants act as living elevators. From the depths of the nest they carry the minute eggs, the maggotlike larvae, and the pupae in their silken cocoons (known erroneously as "ant eggs," and resembling Puffed Rice) to spaces hollowed in the moist soil below boards and flat stones. There the warmth from the sun speeds development without endangering the young by desiccation. If the board is lifted or the stone is rolled aside, the nurse

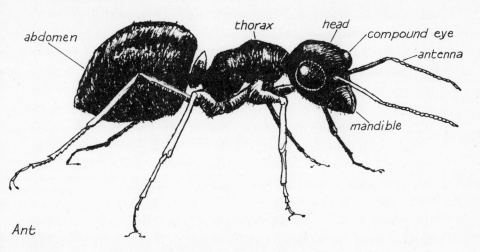

abdomen

thorax

head

compound eye

antenna

mandible

Ant

ants rush to pick up their charges. In jaws like ice tongs they lift each one gently, and run with it into the safety of the soil.

Ant nests often extend five or six feet below the surface. In cold climates they may go even deeper. Earthworms burrow to similar depths to escape from dry air and winter's cold. But when the grass is wet with dew and the air is humid, the worms often stay so close to the surface that robins see them and haul them out.

In fertile soils, the earthworms may have a combined weight exceeding that of all other subterranean animals together. Their tunnels admit oxygen and rain into the depths of the soil. The worms drag fallen leaves and other materials down these avenues, contributing to humus and fertility. The castings distributed by worms at the surface play an important part in the slow recirculation of the soil.

Recently, however, scientists have questioned whether earthworms do more good than harm. The presence of worms may be a measure of fertility rather than a cause of better soil. Certainly each worm engulfs humus and small bits of life such as bacteria, molds, and protozoans along with the sand while extending its tunnels. The sand is discharged in the castings after the worm has digested the other materials. But at least to some extent, the earthworms remove from the soil various substances that might have been useful to green plants, and then to man.

Much of an earthworm's night is spent extended from a burrow mouth, feeling around in all directions for vegetable matter or potential mates. Until recently this habit was believed to be the worm's way of feeding without danger from birds. Then the British naturalist Dr. H. N. Southern hung a red lamp outside the tree hole where a pair of owls was raising a family. He could see the owls in the red light, but the owls—insensitive to red—were unaware that any change had been made in the dark. They brought dozens of earthworms to their nestlings, an observation the naturalist confirmed later by finding in the regurgitated owl pellets immense numbers of glassy bristles used by an earthworm in creeping. Darkness protects earthworms from many predators, but not from owls.

Robins catch earthworms so often while someone is watching by day that we tend to think of these birds as the worms' chief enemy. No one is sure, however, whether the robin sees the worm or hears it at the burrow mouth. In Australia, where earthworms reach a length of 11 feet and a weight of a pound and a half, a person can hear them moving in the soil. Apparently the kookaburra bird (a type of kingfisher) listens intently, too, and uses its strong beak to seize a giant worm. Then the bird braces itself and pulls steadily, bringing several more inches of earthworm into view every time the victim relaxes for a moment.

In America, moles tunnel through the earth after earthworms and insects, often humping up the surface of the ground into miniature mountain ridges. The insects a mole finds are usually the same types a gardener uncovers when digging in the ground. Big white grubs in the shape of a C are the immature stages of the May beetle—the big brown beetle that bangs against the screens at night in early summer. They take a year or two, feeding on the roots of plants, to reach the flying stage and maturity.

The slowest in development of all the insects in the soil

are the young of the periodical cicada, which produces the sirenlike whining call on hot summer days. For seventeen years the curious gnomelike nymphs of this cicada grow, sucking nourishment from tree roots. As many as 84 of these heavy-bodied insects have been counted emerging from a single square foot of ground during a "cicada year." At such times, almost everyone notices the cast skins of the last nymphal stage clinging to tree trunks with claws firmly embedded in the bark. From these the adults have already emerged, flown away swiftly to call, mate, and start another generation on its deliberate way.

The smaller tenants of the soil range downward to microscopic size. They contribute importantly to the welfare of rooted plants through their roles in decay processes which release substances a root can use. So often soil is regarded as being composed only of mineral particles. But each acre of ground to the depth ordinarily turned in plowing contains from five to twenty-five tons of life. Bacteria, molds, and algae are there, providing part of the nourishment for a host of single-celled protozoans, for slender nematode worms, for spiderlike mites, and diminutive insects. The wingless springtails of the soil are so small that, along with the mites, a gardener ordinarily overlooks them.

An Italian entomologist, Dr. A. Berlese, devised a way to take a census of soil animals. Into the small end of a large metal funnel he installed a fine-mesh wire screen. Under the tip of the funnel he hung an open jar of preserving solution. Then into the funnel he shoveled a measured volume of topsoil and hung over it an electric lamp. Light from the continuously-burning bulb kept any soil dwellers from escaping upward. Heat from the lamp, meanwhile, dried out the funnelful of soil—first at the top, then progressively downward toward the wire screen and the collecting jar. The zone of desiccation herded before it every animal able to move. Day after day, night after night, they passed the screen and dropped into the preservative.

The new method proved unbelievably productive. Mites and

spiders, nematodes and segmented worms, insects of many kinds never found before, dropped in great abundance from the shovelfuls of earth. Most of them were minute, and the collection grew for weeks, until the funnel's contents were bone dry all the way down. Above them, in the funnel, countless spores of molds and bacteria remained, along with the dormant stages of algae and animals unable to keep up with the retreating boundary of moist earth.

Denizens of the Forest Floor

Sow bugs, known also as woodlice or slaters, are land crustaceans familiar to most people as oval-bodied, gray-backed, segmented animals that hide for the day under the garbage can or the door mat or a piece of board in the garden. Some of them can curl up into an armored ball, and for this reaction to disturbance they have been called "pill bugs." They are harmless scavengers, running on seven pairs of legs to feast on wet, decaying plant debris.

The number of legs is often a guide to the kind of animal: four pairs on spiders, three pairs on insects. Centipedes are reputed to be "hundred-legged worms" and millipedes "thousand-legged." Centipedes actually may have as few as 12

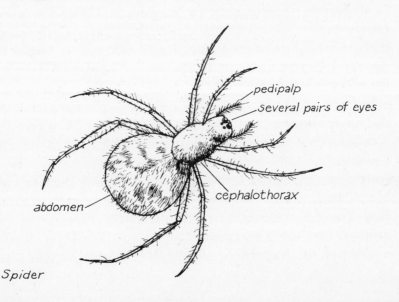

Spider

pairs of legs or as many as 170 pairs. Millipedes vary, too, from 42 to more than 200 pairs—but never a thousand.

Centipedes and millipedes are the companions of sow bugs on woodland soil, and all three types turn up in damp basements. Millipedes are harmless creatures, usually with cylindrical bodies. They travel rather slowly, mincing onward as waves of movement pass forward along the double row of legs. At night, millipedes feed on soft plant materials, or nibble at the decaying remains of some small animal. Most millipedes have glands secreting a material whose odor repels many enemies. But if disturbed, almost any millipede will curl up in a spiral with its head protected at the center and all the legs turned to touch inner turns of its body.

Centipedes should not be trusted any more than spiders, for they have poison claws on the first segment of the body behind the head, and use these in defense as well as to kill prey such as earthworms and insects. A centipede's body is flattened as though to slide more easily under leaves and stones. The legs are attached to the sides, one pair on each segment, rather than below the body as in millipedes, which have two pairs on each segment. Tropical centipedes include kinds reaching eight inches in length.

A far more remarkable find for any tropical explorer is a "walking worm" with 17 to 19 pairs of stubby legs on a soft, caterpillarlike body. This is a peripatus, a type of creature that once roamed all over the Torrid and South Temperate Zones. About 70 kinds of peripatus have survived for more than half a billion years as "living fossils"—links that are not yet missing, between the great group of the arthropods and the phylum of the segmented worms.

A peripatus burrows in the soil, or walks at night and in the rain over jungle floors, or climbs palm trees and hides from dry air among the leaf bases. Few animals are so critical of the humidity. As a peripatus creeps about, it continuously compares the moistness of the air at its head and that at the rear, and seems to be guided in its travels by a definite preference for 95 per cent relative humidity. Ninety per cent

—tentacle

Peripatus

of saturation is too dry, and 100 per cent is unbearably moist.

To some extent this sensitivity to the relative humidity is necessary, for a peripatus loses body moisture to dry air forty times as fast as an insect caterpillar of corresponding size and shape. Its thin skin falls into myriad encircling folds, each pebbled so finely as to suggest a soft cloth. For this reason, a peripatus is sometimes called a "velvet worm."

Unlike a peripatus, which never turns into anything else, an insect caterpillar transforms into a butterfly or moth with wings. It may then be able to fly for several thousand miles on a birdlike migration. Insects were the first animals to conquer the air. Cockroaches, in particular, achieved this distinction more than a quarter of a billion years ago.

Protection from Dry Air

Members of only two great groups of animals can be active for extended periods when the sun is shining and the air is dry. Arthropods with this ability include a tremendous variety of insects, as well as a great many spiders and centipedes that prey upon them. These creatures share the advantages of a lightweight but firm and waterproof covering, jointed appendages, and either a network of inner air tubes (tracheae) carrying oxygen throughout the body or a lunglike pocket full of leaflike plates where the blood can come close to the air without losing much water to it. This body plan has not only permitted these animals to colonize the land, but helped them show more versatility than is to be found elsewhere in the animal kingdom. Insects and spiders are found on all continents, including Antarctica. They thrive from the hottest deserts to the snow-clad peaks of lofty mountains.

The vertebrate style of life also permits occupancy of the land, and is followed among air breathers by adult amphibians and all reptiles, birds, and mammals. Yet it is distinctly second-best, as is shown by the number of kinds following it: less than 30,000, compared with nearly 700,000 types of insects and spiders.

A frog or toad, hopping along or stalking a terrestrial insect, is dependent upon a reserve of water that is just skin-deep. All amphibians wear a private pond just under their loose skins. Broad cavities outside the animals' muscles allow a liquid from the blood to circulate freely. From it the skin cells take water as they need it. But unless a toad is able to burrow into the moist soil or to soak up the dew of night, it shrivels and dies just as surely as a moist-skinned frog that is prevented from splashing into a pond.

These cold-blooded land animals become sluggish in cool weather, and fare better in the southern states than in the North. Other amphibians come to the notice of travelers in the South who see signs offering "BAIT FOR SALE—Worms, Lizards, Minnows." The animals referred to as "lizards" are actually salamanders or newts—the terrestrial adults of amphibians with permanent tails. Their skins are soft and wet, like those of frogs, and provide the principal surfaces where carbon dioxide is exchanged for oxygen. These animals do not suffocate or drown if prevented from using their lungs, but die if their skins become dry. A salamander may even survive being impaled on a hook in the water long enough to attract a fish.

Reptiles Are Land Animals

Reptiles wear a heavier, waterproof skin. They also resemble the birds and egg-laying mammals in producing eggs that contain albumen (the "white"). It is a watery substitute for a private pond surrounding the embryo, while the unhatched reptile grows through stages similar to those of fish and tadpole. Finally the embryo reaches a form that is able to hold up its head and breathe air. The pond turtle, like the sea turtle, the crocodile, and aquatic birds such as gannets and puffins, is a land animal first and a swimmer secondarily. All these animals lay their eggs on land. The young scramble on soil before they reach the water.

Far more than the type of egg and scaly skin distinguish a true lizard from a salamander. Lizards can run, holding their bodies clear of the ground; salamanders merely wriggle, with their wet bellies bearing the weight and their legs giving feeble traction. Lizards can climb and bask in the sun, whereas salamanders must stay in shady woodlands or be active only at night while hunting for worms among the moss and damp leaves.

Lizards often perch on a favorite post or branch, surveying a territory they claim and defend against other lizards. This is particularly evident in Jamaica and other large islands of the West Indies, where each small area seems watched over by some bright-eyed lizard. At the approach of a trespasser of the same or related kind, the claimer of the land draws attention to himself by alternately raising and lowering his head and chest regions, as though exercising by doing "push-ups." At the same time, some of the commonest lizards display a great fold of colored skin below the throat as a distinctive flag from which an intruder can learn the identity of the defender.

In the southeastern United States, the false chameleon, *Anolis,* shows this same habit, with a bright pink throat flag. The body, however, may be leaf green, then cocoa brown, next slate gray, and then green again all within a quarter of an hour. Sometimes this change helps the lizard match its background. More often it provides contrasts. Nor do these lizards appear to rely upon being overlooked. They run rapidly if approached quickly, or while chasing insects as prey.

Farther north and west, the familiar fence lizards, *Scele-porus,* wait for flies to come within snapping distance. Many a child learns that the lizard will move away from an approaching finger, but can be caught easily with a noose

Frilled lizard

fashioned from a slender stem of grass tied to the end of a short stick.

In Texas and other parts of the West, a favorite lizard is the harmless "horned toad" or "horn frog," *Phrynosoma,* an ally of the rancher because of its tremendous appetite for agricultural ants—which keep large areas cleaned of all vegetation and hence useless to livestock. Texas Christian University displays *Phrynosoma* on its coat of arms, and its football team is led to the playing field by the "Horn Frog Band." Horned lizards are usually so docile that a child can carry one in his pocket. Yet, upon occasion, they become so agitated that they eject fine streams of blood from their eyes, to the apparent consternation of some overplayful pup or kitten.

Most lizards depend upon insects and worms as food, but a few are vegetarians. In tropical America, the tree iguanas reach a length of six feet on a diet of foliage, and their white flesh is a favorite food of native peoples. On the Galápagos Islands, straddling the Equator in the Pacific off the coast of Ecuador, marine iguanas swim out a short distance from the rocky coasts to feed on seaweeds. Otherwise they live on land as we do.

North America has the world's only poisonous lizards. One is the two-foot, thick-tailed Gila monster, *Heloderma suspectum,* named for the Gila River in Arizona. The other is the three-foot, slender-tailed Mexican beaded lizard, *Heloderma horridum.* Both animals are desert dwellers, feeding on insects and the eggs of ground-nesting birds. They are so conspicuous that human beings are rarely bitten by them. Even then, the lizard must be provoked into attacking man. In captivity, a Gila monster soon becomes accustomed to handling, and feeds daintily from a raw egg, biting gingerly through the shell, and then licking out the contents with a long flexible tongue.

The *Heloderma* lizard has teeth but no fangs. When it strikes, it is at lightning speed—far different from its normal sluggish movements. The animal holds firmly to its victim, chewing venom into the wound from a row of poison glands along each side of the lower jaw.

Both these lizards have a pebbled skin and blunt muzzles. The Mexican animal is mottled cream and black; its mouth and tongue are pink. The Gila monster is pink and gray, but its mouth and tongue are black. Arizona recently passed a law protecting Gila monsters as a curiosity to be preserved alive for future generations of visitors to see. No other poisonous animal in the world is protected on this basis.

The only other venomous reptiles are some of the snakes. All snakes are carnivorous, but most of them subdue their prey without use of poison. Anglo-America has its venomous snakes: the coral snake, the copperhead, the cottonmouth moccasin, and more than twenty different kinds of rattlesnakes. Yet death from snake bite is rarer than from lightning on the golf links. This is partly because poisonous snakes are exterminated systemically in all populated areas.

In India, where religious beliefs forbid the killing of any kind of life, the venomous cobras are common. They hunt for rats in the houses and protect the area around the heaps of vegetable rubbish in which they lay their eggs. In consequence, at least 5,000 people die of cobra bites every year in India.

The greenish yellow asp of Egypt is a cobra that reaches a length of six and a half feet. The rest of Africa is home to another cobra, the mamba, which climbs trees and attains a length of fourteen feet. This is still four feet short of the record for king cobras in India, southern China and the Philippines.

The coral snake of the southern United States, Mexico, and Central America has a venom similar to that of cobras— one that destroys the nervous system of victims. Fortunately, the coral snake is fairly docile. Full-grown three-foot individuals are both uncommon and conspicuously banded in vivid red, bright yellow, and black. No deaths from coral snake bite are on record in the United States. Captive king cobras of large size, however, inject so much venom in one bite that a man dies of it within an hour.

The poison of the rattlesnake, copperhead, and water moccasin is of an entirely different type, one affecting the victim's blood vessels and ability to form a blood clot. Without treatment, one person in every eight bitten by a large rattlesnake dies of the accident. With treatment, the mortality falls to one in every thirty. Death within less than 24 hours is unusual. All these snakes are like the six-foot fer-de-lance and 12-foot bushmaster of the American tropics in having a pair of large, hinged, hollow fangs at the front of the upper jaw. In striking, the mouth is opened widely, the fangs raised until they are directed straight forward and can be driven into the victim. Contraction of muscles over venom sacs in the roof of the mouth expels the poison through the hollow fangs, releasing as much as a spoonful of the clear amber liquid into the tissue spaces between the skin and body of the prey.

The world's largest snakes are the nonvenomous constrictors, which throw coils of their muscular bodies around prey and crush it so vigorously that it cannot breathe and soon suffocates. Then the snake engulfs its meal, taking it whole as all snakes do, by working the flexible jaws around the victim. For a giant anaconda (water boa) in tropical Amer-

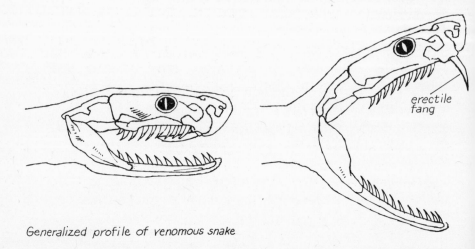

erectile
fang

Generalized profile of venomous snake

ica, the prey may be a wild pig or a small deer; this snake reaches a length of 30 feet and a weight of more than 250 pounds. The regal python of Burma, Malaya, and the Philippines is more slender but sometimes longer—to a record size of 33 feet and 175 pounds. By comparison with these snakes the 15-foot *Boa constrictor* of tropical America is unspectacular. The Indian python reaches a length of 30 feet, the rock python of Africa, 25 feet, the Australian diamond python or "carpet snake," as much as 20 feet. All these snakes can be savage and dangerous if disturbed, but their meat is often relished by natives. It tastes somewhat like veal.

Most of the world's snakes are valuable allies of man and deserve complete protection. They guard his crops by catching rats, mice, gophers, insects, snails, and slugs. Harmless water snakes catch fish, yet seldom take any that are of interest to fishermen. Land snakes such as the garter snake sometimes dine on frogs, toads, and earthworms, but the benefits conferred on man almost always outweigh any detrimental activity.

The absence of limbs, the lack of a breastbone, and of any encircling bony girdles in a snake's body are all put to good use, permitting the ribs to spread open as far as the elastic body wall and skin will stretch. Even the jawbones are linked flexibly, and can be separated from the skull while the snake is swallowing an animal whose diameter is larger than its own.

Turtles show almost the opposite extreme in flexibility. Most of them are encased firmly in a bony shell, and are able to move only the head, neck, legs and tail. When disturbed, the turtle may pull all these extensions of its body into cavities around the shell. At such times it cannot breathe, for ventilation of its lungs depends upon the head and legs being extended while movement of adjacent soft parts of the body wall alternately increase and decrease the volume inside the shell.

A turtle's bony armor is composed of closely fitted plates each of which is enlarged as the animal grows. Overlying the bone and exposed to the surface, most turtles have an additional layer of horny sheaths secreted by the skin. These do not correspond in pattern to the underlying bony plates, but frequently do show concentric marks suggesting the annual rings by means of which the age of a tree can be learned.

Largest of all turtles are the land tortoises of the Galápagos Islands. These club-footed, dome-shelled creatures are vegetarians that come to water only to drink or bathe. Today they seem headed for extinction, but at the time when the islands were discovered, Galápagos tortoises were so abundant that in 1617 William Dampier wrote that "five or six hundred men might subsist on them for several months without any other sort of provisions. They are so extraordinarily large and fat, and so sweet, that no pullet eats more pleasantly." Two of these animals, brought in 1929 to the Brookfield Zoo near Chicago, Illinois, grew by 1955 to weigh nearly 400 pounds. On the islands, their 40-inch shells are sometimes used for bathtubs. A life span of 200 years seems possible for such giants. Smaller turtles probably seldom reach half that age.

Alligators, which are much less active than crocodiles appear to live longer. In captivity both the Chinese and the American alligator have survived for fifty years. A crocodile from the Orinoco River of Venezuela lived twenty-two years, and a Nile crocodile twenty. Older ones may be found in the wild.

Crocodilians include not only the alligators and crocodiles but also seven kinds of alligatorlike caimans in the river systems of tropical America and a slender-snouted gavial in India. All these animals lay their eggs on land, but live much of their lives half submerged in coastal salt water or in rivers and marshes. As young they feed on aquatic insects, crustaceans, snails, and little fishes. At intermediate ages they take more frogs, snakes, and larger fishes. Still older individuals add to their diet a variety of mammals and birds that come to the water's edge. Very large alligators and crocodiles sometimes capture a deer or a cow, usually seizing it by the nose as it takes a drink, dragging it into the water and drowning it.

Crocodiles in Africa rank second only to cobras as reptiles causing human deaths. In India the crocodiles of the Ganges often nab pilgrims bathing in the holy river. America has a crocodile in the Florida Everglades and Keys, but no proven records of human deaths caused by it. At present, alligators and crocodiles are both on the list of protected animals in Florida.

All crocodilians seem to enjoy floating like logs, with only the nostrils, eyes, and ears above the water surface. They propel themselves slowly by gentle paddling with the feet or a slow undulation of the armored tail. Or they haul themselves out on an area of bare bank and sunbathe while facing the water, ready to rush into it if disturbed.

Modern crocodilians are more like mammals than any other reptile. Although they are cold-blooded, their heart is four-chambered and a palate separates the mouth from the nasal passages (in all other reptiles and amphibians, the nostrils open directly into the front of the mouth). At the same time, the crocodilians represent a very ancient style of life, for their scarcely different ancestors were contemporaries of the great dinosaurs and of the earliest warm-blooded animals, the birds and mammals.

Birds Are Land Animals

The earliest birds had teeth and, like the flying reptiles of the day, apparently chased insects on the wing. None of the 8,616 modern kinds of birds has teeth, although many of them still use their hard bills in catching insects. All of them wear an insulating layer of feathers and, like mammals, have a four-chambered heart and essentially constant body temperature.

Flightless birds are so exceptional that, even though they live only in the Southern Hemisphere, they are usually familiar to most people: the swimming penguin, which feeds almost exclusively on fish caught under water; the powerful, running birds, the ostrich of Africa, rhea of South America, emu of Australia, and cassowary of New Guinea and adjacent islands as well as Australia; and the strange, nocturnal kiwi of New Zealand, which has no trace of wings and uses its slender bill for probing in the earth in search of earthworms and burrowing insects.

A male ostrich may stand eight feet tall and weigh 200 pounds; it is the largest of living birds. Only the equally flightless moas of New Zealand and the gigantic *Aepyornis* of Madagascar, both extinct for the last few thousand years, were taller and heavier. Egg shells of *Aepyornis*, still reasonably intact, have been found in caves. They may have been taken there by prehistoric people who used them as vessels for storing water. African natives collect ostrich egg shells for this purpose today. Some *Aepyornis* eggs have measured thirteen inches in length and nine in diameter, with an individual volume equal to several ostrich eggs or to dozens of hen's eggs.

More than 99½ per cent of the world's different kinds of birds can fly. About half of them have feet suitable for perching on tree branches. When the bird's weight rests on its feet, it pulls tendons that clamp toes around the support. Consequently the bird cannot fall off its perch while asleep. To release itself, it must actually leap into the air and take its weight off the feet.

The perching birds are also "song birds," making a variety of distinctive calls enjoyed by a large number of people. Sparrows, thrushes, vireos, wrens, tanagers, warblers, are among the many song birds which live as helpless young in characteristic nests. In Anglo-America they are protected as interesting neighbors, valuable to mankind because of the number of weed seeds and harmful insects they eat.

Some birds appear to be natural clowns. The toucans of the American tropics use their lightweight but tremendous bills in elaborate posturing. Parrots and macaws and Australian budgerigars (shell parakeets or "love birds") are so imitative that they can be taught to repeat words and phrases well enough to be identified. And fishermen never cease to be amused by the pelicans, which are always ready to use their

Aepyornis (about 9 feet tall)

greatly expansible throat pouch to funnel in a meal of fish or fish remains.

There are no naturally blind birds, although a few nest in the darkness of caves. Vision is always highly developed, and sense of smell is usually negligible. The region of the brain attending to coordination of movements in flight is particularly extensive; it serves also the special wealth of instinctive activities, such as courtship, nest-building, and migration.

Vision is so important to most birds that essentially all space in the skull not needed by brain and ears is given over to the eyes. Often the eyeballs are so large that they almost rub against one another as they turn in their sockets. An owl's eyes face forward, allowing good binocular vision. They are also elongated and fixed in the head, requiring the owl to swivel its whole head to shift its gaze. As a result, an owl can rotate its head through more than a full circle. If a person walks around an owl on a low limb, the bird's head continues to follow, letting the owl keep close watch. At a point shortly after the owl has faced directly backward, the limit of head movement is reached. Like a flash, the owl swivels its head through 360 degrees and continues to watch its visitor. Unless the bird watcher chances to see this sudden adjustment, he might conclude that the owl would eventually wind its head off—turning it around and around, as though wringing its own neck.

Mammals of the Land

The only mammals that have achieved flapping flight are the bats, nocturnal animals to which vision is unimportant. Insect-eating bats find and pursue their erratically flying prey by echolocation. The bat produces a series of staccato chirps of high intensity at a pitch far above any the human ear can detect. The echoes of these chirps, returning to the bat from its target insect, tell the flying mammal how big the prey is, give its exact location, and guide the bat in pursuit.

Tropical bats include many kinds that hunt out flowers open at night, there to feast on nectar and pollen and accomplish pollination for the plant. Other bats eat fruit. A few kinds fly low over the surface of ponds and streams, and appear able to detect echoes where the water is ruffled by small fishes just below the surface; these bats reach their feet into the water and catch fish.

Many people have a superstitious dislike for bats, even when informed that all of these flying mammals in temperate climes are important destroyers of mosquitoes and other harmful insects. The small tropical vampire bat is an exception, deserving its reputation. It is unique in alighting gently on a sleeping mammal (or a person), using its razor-sharp teeth to cut through the skin, then lapping up the blood flowing from the wound.

Probably most large mammals can spare an occasional meal of blood to a vampire, for the bat actually takes very little. But its saliva prevents the blood from clotting, and the wound continues to bleed for some time after the bat has left. Moreover, vampires often carry rabies, and transmit this dangerous virus disease to their victims. For this reason they should be feared by people who sleep behind unscreened open windows in the tropics.

True flight is possible for bats because their forelimbs consist of a slender skeleton with tremendously long fingers giving stiffness to a thin, leathery wing membrane. With these collapsible wings, a bat can engage in acrobatics no bird is able to mimic: sudden stops, sidewise movements, backward flying, all under the most exquisite control. Yet when a bat settles for the day, it hangs inverted, its wings folded around it like a cloak. Bat babies, while very young, are carried clinging to the mother's fur as she flies after food. Later they are left at the roost, to await her return.

All mammals emerge into the world at such a tender stage that the mother must feed them from her mammary glands. Even the two egg-laying mammals of Australia and Tasmania, the spiny anteater *Tachyglossus* (found also on New Guinea) and the duckbill platypus *Ornithorhynchus*, secrete milk which the hatchlings lick from their mother's fur.

Except for the opossums of America, all of the world's pouched mammals, (marsupials) are native to New Guinea, Australia, and Tasmania. There they are born as mere pear-shaped beginnings. Their claw-set forelimbs are precociously sturdy and suited to clambering, but no sign of hind legs or tail or ears or eyes can be found. With the strange little body acting as a plumb bob, each climbs into the special pouch (marsupium) and searches for a long nipple it can swallow. For weeks thereafter, each remains clamped to the mother, in the security of the pocket on her underside.

Marsupials take advantage of a wide variety of foods. Kangaroos feed on grasses and low shrubs, much as a cow or deer might do. The koala "bear" specializes on the foliage of a few kinds of eucalpytus tree. Bandicoots are insect-eaters, the Tasmanian "wolf," a doglike predator. Phalangers resemble flying squirrels and, like them, glide from tree to tree. Australian "cats" are marsupials, too, and so are mouse-like, ratlike, and burrowing molelike animals in this part of the world.

Most mammals are like mankind in spending weeks or months prior to birth linked to the mother by a placenta—a special tissue that permits free exchange of food and oxygen from the mother's blood for wastes and carbon dioxide from the blood of the embryo. Placental mammals need no pouch when they are born. At that time they have both arms and legs equally well developed and, unlike marsupials, are capable of nursing without swallowing the nipple.

Almost a century ago, the great English anatomist Sir Richard Owen is reported to have boasted: "Give me a tooth, and I will reconstruct the mammal." Many a modern scientist follows in his footsteps and can make good the claim, for placental mammals differ markedly in their teeth and in the favored foods on which they bite. In all of them, however, the teeth are of the same types found in the human mouth: incisors at the front; then a single canine tooth above and below on each side; and a series of teeth (premolars and molars) that in man are used for real chewing. Even such details as the number of incisors between the canines are important: the shrew, the bat, and the cat have six incisors where we have but four.

The most diminutive of mammals—the shrews—are also most similar to the earliest mammals on earth. With little pointed teeth of each type they dine on earthworms, insects, millipedes, and other small animals caught in hurried nocturnal hunting. Underground, their close kin the moles seek a similar diet. The European hedgehog in its coat of spines chooses comparable food to match its teeth. All these animals are grouped in the Insectivora.

The cat that catches a shrew has teeth fitted for tearing flesh. They are sharp, with the canines enlarged into fangs. The dog and the hyena, the raccoon and the mink, the skunk and the bear are similarly equipped. All can pounce upon or chase their prey, able to see where they are going with eyes that are forward-facing. Or they may trail a victim, using a keen sense of smell. They are members of the Carnivora, a clan represented in the sea by seals, sea lions, and the walrus with its enormous upper canines as tusks.

Our own teeth match more closely those of apes and monkeys, the tarsier of the East Indies, and the lemurs and kin of lands from southern Asia into Africa. Of this whole assembly, only man, the gorillas, and the baboons live on the ground. Full-grown gorillas appear too heavy to climb far. Other members of the Primates are tree-dwellers, and there make fine use of opposable thumbs in grasping branches as they romp about. The opposable thumb and manipulative hand allow all primates to examine objects closely. A disproportionately large brain (especially in regions where movements are controlled) and ability to learn from experience go with the dexterous hands. Keen vision matches interest in objects handled, and is important for life among the branches. Sight can be more useful than the sense of smell in finding a way around, and infinitely more valuable in judging the distance to the next limb.

Primates are unusual in having nails, instead of claws, on some fingers and toes. Monkeys in the New World also have their long (prehensile) tails under such wonderful control that they use them like a fifth hand while they clamber with great versatility far above the ground.

Rabbits and hares have four incisors in the upper jaw, two in the lower—a difference seldom evident unless the mouth is wide open. Of the four in the upper jaw, one pair is situated behind the other. Canine teeth are absent altogether. These features in the mouth seem to go with a tail reduced to a mere powder puff, and hind legs capable of propelling the animal at high speed, one leap after another. Baby hares are born in a full coat of fur, and are able to hop after the mother immediately. Young rabbits are naked and helpless; the mother hides them in a nest made partly with fur pulled from her own coat.

Two chisel-like incisor teeth above and below, with gaps

where the canines are missing, are the trademark of the rodents, such as mice and rats, porcupines and chinchillas, beavers, gophers, and squirrels. In all these animals the incisor teeth continue to grow from the roots, and are self-sharpening. With them a beaver can fell a tree two feet in diameter, a rat can gnaw through concrete two feet thick, and a squirrel can get the last fragment of food out of an acorn. Rodents comprise fully a fifth of all the kinds of mammals, and compete far too successfully with man in many ways all over the world.

Hoofed mammals have either six or eight incisors in the lower jaw, and well-developed grinding teeth farther back. The first set of teeth ("baby teeth" or milk dentition) are replaced so gradually by the second set (adult dentition) that man has learned to judge the age of domesticated kinds of hoofed mammals by examining the inside of the mouth. Additional indications of age can be found in the teeth because those used for grinding wear away at a fairly steady rate.

A "parted hoof" is the mark of the even-toed hoofed mammals, which set two or four toes on the ground. Those that do not chew the cud include the various kinds of pigs and peccaries, and the hippopotamus. In these animals the canines of the lower jaw are present, often enlarged into tusks used in fighting and in self-defense.

A cud-chewer (ruminant) may be an antelope, cow, deer, sheep, or their many kin, including the tallest animal of all today, the giraffe. These animals lack upper incisors and the canines in both jaws. The lower incisors are pressed against a firm pad in the upper jaw while the animal grazes or browses. The food, however, is not chewed at once. It is swallowed and received by the first part (rumen) of the three- or four-chambered stomach. This is a huge mixing bowl in which the fresh vegetation becomes mixed with special bacteria that can digest the cellulose of which plant cell walls are composed.

By the time mixing in the rumen is complete, the cud-chewer is ordinarily somewhere at ease. The second chamber

of the stomach then packages a lump of the mixture. The ruminant regurgitates this as a cud, and chews it thoroughly. When the plant fibers are well broken and the live bacteria worked through the soft mass, it is swallowed again and conducted into the third portion of the stomach, where the bacteria and the animal's digestive juices work together on the food.

The odd-toed hoofed mammals put on the ground a single toe on each foot (as do horses and zebras), or three (if they are tapirs), or all five (in rhinoceroses). All these animals have incisor teeth in both jaws and bite, both while severing vegetation and in self-defense.

Elephants are special. Not only are they the largest of land animals, but their noses extend into the form of a trunk as much as seven feet long, with which the animal can tear down a tree or pick up a pin, accept a peanut or hose its great body down with water. An elephant's grinding teeth are well developed and intricately folded in both jaws, presenting serpentine patterns of hard enamel against the coarse food. The upper canines usually extend into tusks used in digging and fighting. They are the chief source of ivory, and may weigh more than 225 pounds per pair—fifteen to twenty times as much as the brain.

CHAPTER
4

How Animals Live

To save its life, an animal may ignore thirst and hunger for a time, or even hold its breath. For minutes or hours a hippopotamus, a loon, or a land turtle will remain hidden under water, until its need for oxygen is more desperate than its fear of attack.

Every living cell must have a continuous supply of energy. To obtain energy in a usuable form, almost all animal cells carry on the common kind of respiration, for which oxygen is necessary. Ordinarily, they get their oxygen either as we do, from the atmosphere, or as a fish does, from the gas dissolved in the water around them. Single-celled animals and those of comparatively simple construction, such as sponges, coral animals, and flatworms, require only modest amounts of oxygen. Their needs for the dissolved gas are satisfied without effort on their part because oxygen diffuses from the surrounding water into their bodies. Embryos developing inside eggs depend for at least a short time upon oxygen reaching them by diffusion from outside the egg shell. Some of the smallest mites, spiders, and terrestrial insects live for a few days after they emerge from the egg with no special way to increase the rate at which they get oxygen from their environment.

A few creatures, living in the bottom mud of deep lakes or in the digestive tract of a larger animal, have almost no oxygen available to them in dissolved form. These animals, such as the "blood worms" (midge insect larvae) and tapeworms, get their energy from food materials such as sugars by using a wasteful method of respiration without oxygen. They are said to be "anaerobic."

Larger and more complex animals have greater needs for oxygen, matching the increased number of living cells and weight of protoplasm. Cells far from the body surface must have oxygen brought to them, either by a circulating blood (as in ourselves) or by way of branching air tubes which reach all parts of the body (as in most insects, centipedes, and millipedes).

Most of the larger animals use their muscles in bringing oxygen close to delicate moist membranes where it can be exchanged for carbon dioxide. These breathing movements are familiar in land vertebrates, whether mammal, bird, reptile, or amphibian, whose lungs provide the place for gas exchange. Lungs are actually blind pockets connected to the outside world through the floor of the digestive tract in the mouth or throat region. Special arteries bring from the body to the lungs the blood that is charged with carbon dioxide but poor in oxygen. After the exchange, other arteries carry away the same blood toward the body cells, bringing them oxygen and being ready to pick up another load of carbon dioxide. Land snails and spiders use lungs of somewhat similar form and action.

Gills serve in place of lungs for water animals such as cyclostomes (such as the lamprey), fishes, and the tadpole stage of amphibians. Blood vessels from the heart branch within the thin-skinned gills, providing an opportunity for exchange of dissolved gases between the blood and the water passing the gills. Cleared of its carbon dioxide and rich in oxygen, the blood goes on to the rest of the body. Cyclostomes and cartilaginous fishes, such as sharks and rays, have several gill openings along each side of the body, whereas the gills of familiar bony fishes are concealed under a protective gill cover. Amphibian tadpoles usually hatch from the egg with external gills, but these become covered by a fold of skin that grows backward, leaving only a small opening through which water can escape.

The lamprey, a common cyclostome, can inhale and exhale water through its gill openings; in this way it breathes while its circular, jawless mouth is attached as a sucker. Most sharks, by contrast, must keep swimming to produce a current of water through the mouth and out past the gills; if prevented from swimming they suffocate. Bony fishes and tadpoles gulp water. Some of them have membranous valves just inside the lips, serving to keep the liquid moving in one direction—through the gills and out under the edge of the gill cover.

An adult frog or toad uses the floor of its mouth as a pump with which to push air into its lungs. It presses its lips together firmly, making an air-tight seal, and then lets the floor of its mouth sag. This pulls air into the mouth through the nostrils. Valves in the nostrils close; the floor of the mouth is pulled up by muscular contraction, and the air is forced into the lungs. This is "pressure breathing." To exhale, the amphibian opens the valves between lungs and mouth and in the nostrils; the air rushes out because it is under pressure.

Turtles and tortoises that are encased in a hard shell suck air into their lungs by movements of the flexible skin at armpits and leg bases. Marine turtles take small breaths of air, but most of them depend upon a supplementary breathing movement that takes water containing oxygen into the cloaca —a pocket into which the digestive tract and urogenital systems empty. This supplement permits them to stay below the water surface for longer periods.

Other reptiles use muscles to alter the position of their

ribs, changing the dimensions of the body, sucking in air by expanding the lungs. This is "vacuum breathing." When the muscles relax, the gas is exhaled. Birds depend upon very rapid breathing movements of this kind, and gain efficiency through having a number of blind air sacs connected to the lungs. After a bird exhales in each cycle of breathing, its lungs still contain gas rich in carbon dioxide and poor in oxygen; this gas is "residual air" that has come to the lungs from the air sacs. At inhalation, however, the residual air is driven back into the air sacs and a completely fresh supply of "tidal air" fills the lungs.

Mammals possess no comparable air sacs, and the tidal air merely dilutes the residual air. Perhaps as a compensation, they have a tent-shaped muscular diaphragm extending across the body cavity, helping to move a larger volume of tidal air at each breath. When the diaphragm contracts, it becomes flatter and enlarges the chest cavity, aiding the rib movements in producing space in which the elastic lungs can expand. Exhalation occurs when both the diaphragm and the muscles between the ribs relax.

By contracting its abdominal muscles, pressing the organs of the abdominal cavity against the diaphragm and the diaphragm against the lungs, a mammal can force air out more rapidly. The hiss of a frightened cat and the controlled blowing of a bassoon by a skillful musician arise in this way.

After the blood is aerated, the heart pumps it to all parts of the body. In vertebrates, the oxygen that is gained in the lungs or the gills passes rapidly into the red blood cells. There it combines loosely with hemoglobin—the iron-bearing protein that gives blood its color. When the blood reaches the various parts of the body, the oxygen separates from the hemoglobin and the dissolved gas diffuses into the tissues. While oxygen is linked to hemoglobin, the color is bright red. But after the oxygen has been released, the hemoglobin changes to a purplish red. The red cells allow the blood to carry about fifty times as much oxygen as it could otherwise. To carry the same amount of oxygen without red cells, there would have to be about fifty times as much blood in the body. A great deal of energy would be needed just to carry around so much blood.

Carbon dioxide from respiration in the cells is carried by the blood to the lungs or the gills or the skin. Part of this waste material travels in solution, and part in the form of carbonates—compounds that change readily and release carbon dioxide again where the blood can exchange it for oxygen.

Segmented worms, such as earthworms, owe their reddish color to hemoglobin in the blood. The pigment is dissolved, however, and not in cells; it seems to be of far less importance in respiration. Among arthropods, such as lobsters and insects, the oxygen-carrying substance dissolved in the blood is usually hemocyanin—a copper-bearing protein that is bright blue when loaded with oxygen but almost colorless otherwise.

The Internal Water Pool

The largest single constituent of any animal is water. Depending upon the kind of creature, the proportion may be anywhere from 25 to more than 95 per cent. Many insects come close to the lower figure, and jellyfishes to the higher one. Yet each kind of animal has its own limits. It soon dies if its internal water supply shrinks beyond a critical point. Nor can it tolerate too much water among its cells.

Anglers all know that their "fishworms" must be kept in a container with moist earth, for these creatures have little protection against dry air. So long as the humidity is high, as in the can or a burrow or over a lawn on a summer night or during a daytime rain, the earthworm can be active. But a few hours' exposure to warm dry air is fatal to it. The cylindrical soft body shrivels to become a brittle flattened ribbon, and no amount of soaking will bring the earthworm to life again.

A frog can manage only a little better in dry air, for its

moist skin loses water rapidly and the body holds only a limited supply. If a frog escapes from a moist terrarium into a dry room, it is usually found a day or two later as a lifeless mummy whose parched skin stretches so tightly over the skeleton that one wonders where the muscles and internal organs have gone.

The thicker skins of reptiles, birds, and mammals protect the water store of the body much more efficiently. It is no accident that these are the true land vertebrates. In all of them, only the innermost layer of skin cells is alive. Outside this layer the cells have died in becoming filled with waterproof oils and waxes. These dead cells are easily worn off, or they may be shed periodically in a single continuous sheet, as a snake does. Far fewer glands are found in the skin of a land vertebrate than in that of an amphibian or fish.

The insects, which are the most successful style of land animal, gain much of their versatility because they have a delicate skin that secretes a comparatively thick, nonliving, waterproof covering in the form of a lightweight shell. Flexibility is maintained by producing this armor in bands or plates connected by flexible membranes. But the shell is so firm that growth has to be intermittent. The old shell is shed

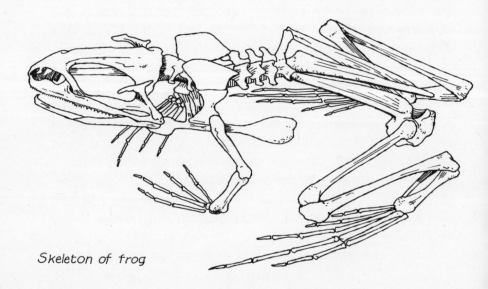

Skeleton of frog

before a new one, formed by the same delicate skin, hardens in a larger size. At each molt, the insect is flabby, unarmored, and vulnerable both to enemies and to desiccation.

The most conspicuous part of the water pool in any animal with a circulatory system is the blood. An insect or a mollusk propels it by a muscular heart, but for much of each slow circuit the blood seeps between the body organs in vague spaces. In segmented worms and vertebrates, however, the blood is driven through distinct arteries which are connected by a tremendous network of fine capillary vessels to the veins. The capillaries, like the tissue spaces, are the real sites of exchange for materials carried by the blood. In them oxygen is swapped for carbon dioxide, carbon dioxide for oxygen, digested foodstuffs are obtained from the wall cells of the alimentary canal and distributed to the rest of the body, wastes are picked up and discharged, and hormones enter from the glands of internal secretion to be carried as chemical messages to regions of special sensitivity.

Blood is far more than a suspension of red cells in water containing dissolved gases, carbonates, products of digestion, wastes, and hormones—although all of these are present. It is easy to separate the cells from the suspending liquid, the plasma. But the plasma is still yielding to scientists many other chemical compounds of importance to the animal.

The blood contains also white cells which are able to move about under their own power, and to escape from the capillaries into the tissue spaces. White cells are important in policing the body for dying cells or invaders such as bacteria, which they can destroy. The plasma contains other protective agents: protein materials called gamma globulins, which aid the white cells in neutralizing the effects of disease organisms, viruses, and such foreign substances as venoms.

It is essential, of course, that an animal protect its blood. If an accident tears a gap in the body and too much blood escapes, the animal dies. Different animals have various ways of avoiding loss of blood and life in this way. Among vertebrates the blood plasma contains a number of materials serving as a clotting mechanism. When the blood comes in contact with foreign objects it can wet, or with juices crushed from damaged body cells, the clotting mechanism goes into action. It produces a mesh of fine threads (fibrin), which form a dam and trap red cells, forming a clot. Usually it staunches the flow of blood and allows body cells the time needed to heal over the wound. Blood from which the cells and clotting mechanism have been removed is a clear amber color, and is known as serum.

Ever since 1628, when the English physician William Harvey proved that the blood in a human heart makes a complete circuit through arteries, capillaries, veins, and back to the heart again, everyone is told how these blood vessels form a continuous circulatory system. Seldom does anyone mention that the system normally leaks. Yet a gradual flow is maintained by this leakage, a flow between the internal organs (viscera), among the muscles in the arms and legs, and also just below the skin. The red cells do not escape from the vessels, but the watery plasma seeps through the capillary walls into the tissue spaces and is then called lymph. Or it passes into the cavities within the brain and around the spinal cord, forming the cerebrospinal fluid.

Lymph travels slowly along vague routes, eventually finding its way back into the blood vessels. It enters the veins where the blood pressure is lowest—near the heart—only to form again where the pressure is high and the walls of the vessels are just one cell thick—in the capillaries.

The sluggish lymphatic circulation picks up dead cells, invading bacteria and injected poisons such as those from a mosquito bite or a bee sting, and reduces their damage to a minimum. At intervals along the lymph channels are swellings called lymph nodes, where white cells (here known as lymphocytes) devour bacteria, and where other cells secrete the gamma globulins.

Blood and lymph and cerebrospinal fluid form an internal environment for the cells of the body. They are a rich reservoir from which the cells take nourishment, and serve also as a drain for dissolved wastes that can be discharged later from kidneys, lungs, and skin.

Into this reservoir or internal water pool goes the moisture from food and drink, and the water that penetrates the skin of an aquatic animal. From the pool the kidneys (or the equivalent organs in invertebrate animals) withdraw and discharge to the outside of the body enough water to keep the reservoir within its proper dimensions. This activity is self-adjusting, matching any unusual intake through greater excretion of water.

If the reservoir begins to shrink through water loss that is not compensated by water intake, the kidneys reduce their activity and the output of urine decreases. This happens during prolonged thirst, or when perspiration is excessive, or when water is lost through too rapid discharge of undigested wastes (diarrhea). By keeping the output of water through all avenues equal to the intake of more water, the blood and lymph and cerebrospinal fluid remain in equilibrium with the cells of the body.

The Great Disassembly Line

The cells of every animal's body need a vast array of chemical substances, in addition to oxygen and water. These other materials are foods, from which energy and building materials can be obtained for maintenance and growth. Some foods, such as the mineral iodine and vitamins, are needed only in minute amounts. Others the animal must procure much more plentifully.

The food an animal eats rarely supplies it with the exact chemical compounds its cells require. For this reason, most animals must convert their food into usable compounds, and use fairly simple components for producing more of their own kind of protoplasm and secretions. Most animals accomplish the first major changes while their food is passing through the alimentary canal. The digestive tract of an animal is a disassembly line, where complex foods are converted into simpler molecules that can be absorbed and used as building blocks.

Digestion consists of chemical changes occurring in water. Part of an animal's water pool, in fact, consists of liquid in its digestive tract. Soon after the food is swallowed, it is mixed with watery secretions and brought to a uniform, fluid consistency by muscular action. While passing along the tube, it usually has the consistency of thick cream. And while undigested residues are being made ready for discharge, the animal ordinarily absorbs much of the water again, solidifying its wastes.

Foods containing carbohydrates, proteins, and fats require extensive disassembly before the products of digestion can be absorbed. The digestive tract handles these carbon-containing foods according to what other elements are present in their composition. Carbohydrates and lipids (fats) contain only carbon, hydrogen, and oxygen, whereas proteins include nitrogen as well.

In carbohydrates, which include starch, glycogen, and sugars, the hydrogen and oxygen are in the same proportions as in water (H_2O). Digestive processes simplify them to molecules with six carbon atoms, as in the formula $C_6H_{12}O_6$. Fruit sugar (fructose) and grape sugar (glucose) have this form. They can be absorbed and used so readily that they are called the "energy sugars."

Sugars produced by digestion are carried in the blood plasma and used by all the cells of the body to provide energy for other chemical processes. Excess amounts of sugar added to the blood may be discarded in the urine by the kidneys or stored as glycogen ("animal starch") by the liver, or transformed into fats and stored.

Lipids, including fats, contain much less oxygen in proportion to hydrogen than is found among carbohydrates. Fats in our food require special treatment before digestion begins, because they do not mix with water and come automatically under the influence of the digestive juices. Bile, the chief secretion of the vertebrate liver, emulsifies fats and holds them in the form of very fine droplets. Fat-splitting digestive agents can act upon the surfaces of these droplets, separating the water-soluble, absorbable products—fatty acids and glycerine. Both of these are taken through the intestinal wall and reach the blood stream. The cells of the body may use the glycerine and fatty acids from the blood in making new fats, or convert these materials into six-carbon sugars and use them as sources of energy.

Proteins are tremendously large molecules, including some of the largest known. During digestion, each protein is fragmented into a series of nitrogen-containing units called amino acids. These dissolve readily in water and can be absorbed through the wall cells of the digestive tract. Among vertebrate animals, the amino acids are distributed by the blood stream, and the cells of the body take from the blood the amino acids they need to build new proteins.

The proteins in body cells provide many of the cells' characteristics. Some proteins are stiff and inert, such as the collagen composing horn, nails and claws, hair and feathers. Others form thin films in the membranes surrounding and inside cells. Still others include the globin part of the red pigment hemoglobin in red blood cells, the albumen ("white") of an egg, and the gamma globulins of blood plasma—the antibodies that give protection against diseases such as smallpox and poliomyelitis.

Many of the proteins inside cells serve as enzymes, without which the important chemical processes of life would not occur. When the specific protein that serves as an enzyme is present, a chemical reaction can proceed at extremely low concentrations of the reacting substances, without much rise in temperature, and with no obvious external source of power, such as electricity.

Animals are unable to manufacture all the enzymes they need unless their diet includes small amounts of carbon-containing compounds called vitamins. These necessary vitamins come from green plants, either directly when the animal eats the green plant or indirectly when it eats definite parts of other animals that have eaten green plants—the parts in which the vitamins have been stored. Unlike animals, the green plants have the ability to manufacture the enzymes they need themselves as well as the vitamins required by animals.

Animals also eat many things that are indigestible. The cherry pit or the glass bead swallowed by a child ordinarily continues through the digestive tube and emerges unchanged. An owl swallows a mouse whole, but does not digest the fur, bones, teeth, or claws. Instead, these are regurgitated in compact pellets that accumulate around the owl's nest. Scientists can learn what prey the owl is catching by studying the pellets.

Plant foods contain large amounts of cellulose, a carbohydrate that forms the cell walls in plants. Guinea pigs live almost entirely upon a plant diet, but are unable to digest the cellulose. Like most other animals, they lack the enzyme with which cellulose can be split into smaller molecules such as starches. Consequently the guinea pig discharges the cellulose as undigested residues in the fecal pellets from the anus.

Cows and other animals that chew the cud are partners with bacteria that produce cellulose-splitting enzymes. Yet a good deal of undigested cellulose remains in their fecal wastes. In many parts of the world where wood, coal, and petroleum products are scarce or expensive, people burn dried cow dung as fuel. In this way they obtain in the form of heat the energy in the cellulose that neither the bacteria nor the cow digested. In other parts of the world, dairy cows are fed special rations that promote the welfare of the bacterial partners, and help the cows get more good from their cellulose-rich food.

Each region of the alimentary canal has its own roles in digestion. Our own tract is typical. In the mouth we begin mixing the food with watery saliva, which contains a starch-splitting enzyme. Breakdown of starches begins as soon as they are mixed with this enzyme. The longer we chew starchy food, the more of it is digested in the mouth.

The gullet passes the food we swallow to the stomach so rapidly that little digestion can be accomplished on the way. The gullet merely conveys the chewed food past the neck and through the chest, past organs such as the lungs and heart, to the stomach.

Digestion of proteins begins in the stomach, through the activity of gastric secretions (pepsin and hydrochloric acid). Liquefaction of the food continues there, and small squirts of the creamlike product are forced by muscular contraction through the valve from the stomach into the small intestine. The digestion of carbohydrates and proteins is completed in the small intestine. It is there, too, that fat digestion both begins and ends. After the six-carbon sugars, amino acids, fatty acids, and glycerine have been absorbed through the wall of the small intestine, the residue is passed into the large intestine or colon. There much of the water and most of the fat-emulsifying agent from the bile are retrieved, the water being returned to the animal's internal pool. The colon also secretes mucus over the residue of undigested matter, rendering it easier to discharge through the anus.

Between the large intestine and the anus, many animals are like ourselves in having a special region of the alimentary canal, the rectum. Ordinarily it is empty. It serves principally to form fecal material into pellets as these are being discharged.

Dissolved Wastes

Each protein in food yields an assortment of amino acids. Some provide a wide variety. Others, such as egg white, are more limited. Yet in eating enough protein food to supply the amino acids it needs for repair and growth, an animal takes in many amino acids in quantities far beyond what it can use. In vertebrate animals, the liver monitors the concentration of each of the twenty-odd different amino acids as they circulate through the blood. Any in excess supply are absorbed by the liver cells and reorganized chemically. The products of this reorganization are sugars, heat, and nitrogenous wastes such as urea. All of these are returned to the blood stream.

The vertebrate kidneys also monitor the concentration of materials in the blood. They accomplish this in two steps. First the kidney capillaries act like coarse sieves, holding back the blood cells and plasma protein molecules, but letting smaller molecules filter into the excretory tubules. Then each kidney salvages from the kidney tubules into the blood most of the water, all of the sodium salts, usually all of the sugar, but almost none of the nitrogen-containing wastes. In consequence, the liquid filtered out by the kidney begins as a cell-free, protein-free blood plasma or lymph, and ends as a urine that is a fairly concentrated solution of nitrogenous wastes—usually urea.

Urea is a soluble compound, easily concentrated in the urine by reabsorption of water. Each urea molecule contains one carbon atom and two of nitrogen, as well as hydrogen and oxygen. Hence the animal that excretes urea expends some of its carbon-containing compounds from food in order to dispose of its nitrogen-containing wastes.

Birds, desert reptiles, insects, and a few other kinds of animals are adapted in a special way that conserves water, which is just an extra load for a flying creature and a rare item in a desert diet. These animals convert their nitrogenous wastes into uric acid. It costs still more in food—five carbon atoms for each four of nitrogen eliminated.

Uric acid is excreted as a paste or as a powder of glistening white crystals, conserving the small water pool inside the body. This first act of a honeybee when, at maturity, it reaches the doorway to the hive, it to turn and discharge a puff of uric acid crystals that represent the accumulated nitrogenous wastes from several weeks of earlier life as larva, pupa, and young adult inside the hive. Here the use of uric acid has the extra advantage that the developing bees do not befoul the hive.

Contraction

Muscular work is one of the most obvious uses of energy by animals. Some muscles are attached to the skeleton and serve in locomotion. Others are associated with the digestive tract or the circulatory system or the reproductive organs, and have importance in shifting food or blood or eggs. The final contribution a human mother gives her unborn child is a muscular shove that pushes it out into the world.

All living cells have some ability to contract. Muscle cells merely specialize in this type of work. Curiously enough, once a muscle cell has contracted, it cannot extend itself again. The force of gravity or the pressure of a fluid or the pull of some opposing muscle is necessary to extend a relaxed muscle and ready it for another contraction. For this reason, muscles ordinarily work at least in pairs. One set of muscles tilts the human head backward; another set works with gravity in pulling the chin downward. If we go to sleep while sitting upright, both sets of muscles relax. Gravity, now unopposed, causes the head to nod forward.

Each muscle is composed of thousands of separate contractile cells. Each muscle cell follows an all-or-none principle, either remaining so unstimulated that it does not contract, or contracting fully—and then relaxing again. If a few muscle cells in a muscle contract simultaneously, the whole muscle pulls gently. If more muscle cells contract at the same time, a stronger pull is exerted. Except in extreme situations, a muscle does not exert its maximum effect. Yet because only part of the population of muscle cells contracts at any given moment, the whole muscle can provide a continuous pull. The cells composing it take turns at contracting, relaxing, being extended, and contracting again, with a fairly steady number excited into contraction at all times.

Each muscle cell in the rested, well-nourished condition contains a supply of glycogen, the carbohydrate known as "animal starch." When stimulated into action, the muscle cell converts some of this glycogen into lactic acid, and in the conversion obtains the energy for contraction. If the cell relaxes and is extended passively, it can call upon the remainder of its glycogen for further contractions, one after another. This action requires no oxygen or other substance from outside the cell. Hence it can be prompt and forceful.

With continued exertion, a muscle cell produces so much lactic acid that nervous excitation can no longer induce contractions. The cell is showing fatigue. If a whole muscle is stimulated repeatedly, one contraction after another with scant rest between, it shows fatigue by refusing to contract. This is not due to laziness but to an actual chemical block to nervous stimulation.

During relaxation and recovery, part of the lactic acid from contraction is carried away by the blood stream. Fatigue disappears. Another fraction of the lactic acid is oxidized ·into carbon dioxide and water, releasing energy, in a process that requires oxygen from the blood stream. The energy is used to change the remaining lactic acid back to the form of glycogen. For full recovery, the muscle cell still needs to absorb sugar from the blood plasma, to manufacture glycogen and rebuild its reserve supply toward future activity.

When a sprinter makes a 100-yard dash, his muscles do their work with little chance to get oxygen or sugar and hence recover. At the end of the run, the sprinter breathes deeply and pays the so-called oxygen debt his muscles have incurred in their burst of activity. But when a man or a horse runs a mile or a bird flies across the Gulf of Mexico nonstop, the blood stream adjusts itself to deliver more oxygen and sugar to the working muscles and to carry off the lactic acid and carbon dioxide. As soon as this adjustment has been made, the runner or flier performs more easily; he has found his "second wind."

Rarely does anyone see a digestive tract propel its contents by waves of muscular contractions. Or a beating heart. Or an egg or a baby emerging into the world, urged along by muscular propulsion. Muscles are seen at work more readily in movements of the body and its appendages. Here, however, their action is less direct, since they are acting by moving parts of the skeleton. It is easy to think of the jointed internal skeleton of a vertebrate animal or the shell of an arthropod as having more importance in muscular movements than in supporting the body. Admittedly, any skeleton does both.

In animals the combination of hinged hard parts and of muscles that move them is an equivalent to the levers recognized by engineers. They are simple machines that make it possible to move weights by applying force on one side or the other of a hinge point. Many muscles do their work by preventing movement, as is seen in those that hold the human head level against the force of gravity. While maintaining the body in a steady position, a muscle has little chance to relax. For this reason, standing still is far more fatiguing than using the same muscles in walking.

Contraction of muscles attached to the skeleton often serves also to push the blood along toward the heart. Vertebrate animals have valves in their veins, preventing the return flow of blood. Whenever a skeletal muscle contracts, shortening and thickening at the same time, it squeezes veins in its close vicinity and moves the blood onward—always in the direction of the heart. This appears to be the reason why shop clerks, who stand still so much of the day, have trouble with sluggish return of blood from the feet and often develop enlarged "varicose" veins in their legs. Postmen, who walk for as many hours a day, are constantly compressing the veins between the muscles of their legs and rarely have difficulty with circulation there.

A comparison of general body form and habits would scarcely lead anyone to expect that the skeleton and associated muscles would bear much similarity in a dog, an elephant, a hippopotamus, a man, a mouse, and a seal. Yet each of these mammals has a skull composed of a jawbone hinged against the cranium, exactly seven units of the backbone (vertebrae) in the neck region, twelve more vertebrae to which paired ribs are attached in the thoracic region, five vertebrae lacking ribs in the lumbar region, five vertebrae joined into an immovable piece to which the hip girdle is anchored in the sacral region, and still more vertebrae in the tail, the caudal region.

The arm and leg of man are representative in having a single long bone meeting the girdle at a ball-and-socket joint:

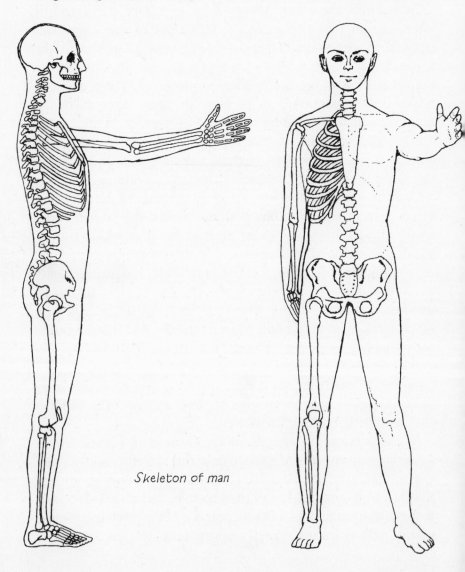

Skeleton of man

the humerus bone in the arm, the femur in the leg. Next in both arm and leg come two bones parallel to each other, hinged to the single bone at elbow and knee respectively. These are the radius and ulna in the arm, the tibia and fibula in the leg. Wristbones and anklebones have many features in common. Still farther from the body, the palm of the hand and the sole of the foot each conceal five series of bones: the metacarpals in the hand, the metatarsals in the foot. Even the bones of the fingers and toes correspond. And throughout the mammals, the muscles moving each bone are organized similarly in their points of attachment at the ends and in their nerve connections.

The hip girdle is actually in two halves meeting on the mid-line. The shoulder girdle is not a true girdle at all since it consists of a right and a left shoulder blade, unconnected to one another. They help hold the arms in place. Both the hip girdle and the shoulder girdle are regarded as parts of the appendages; most of the muscles attached to them are concerned with moving the appendages, whether arm, leg, wing, or flipper.

All mammals, all birds, and some reptiles have a breastbone to which most of the ribs are attached. This supports the chest wall more firmly, without interfering with the movements of the ribs needed in ventilating the lungs. In flying birds, the breastbone is greatly enlarged and keel-shaped, providing broad surfaces to which are attached the flight muscles that pull the wings downward at each beating stroke against the air. Flightless birds, such as the ostrich, may have wings. But their breastbone is flat and said to be "raft-shaped." It serves as an anchor for the ribs and, to some extent, as a shield, valuable when two birds fight.

The breastbone of monkeys, apes, and man is linked on each side to the shoulder girdle by way of the collarbone, which provides useful support when the animal is holding its entire weight by one arm from a tree branch. The collarbone may be broken, however, if a person falls off a horse and strikes the ground shoulder first. In a cat, the correspond-

Skeleton of whale

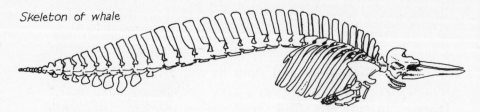

ing bone (the clavicle) extends into the muscles as a mere vestige. This allows the cat to draw its front legs together and pass the body through any hole large enough to pass its head. Occasionally a human being is born without collar-bones. Such a person can bump the shoulders together in front in a most astonishing way.

Body Temperature

Sometimes a person envies a domestic pet its ability to relax so completely. Yet even when a dog or a cat is stretched out sleeping, its skeletal muscles are under slight tension. Some of the muscle cells are contracting at all times. This contraction produces no movement, but it does liberate heat. Work done by the liver and other internal organs produces heat also. The cat and the dog, like any other warm-blooded animal, regulate the rate of heat production and also, to some extent, the rate of heat loss from the body.

When the outside temperature is low, the animal tends to lose heat to it. The rate of heat loss can be reduced if the feathers or fur are raised by muscular contraction, trapping a deeper blanket of air next to the skin. Our own skins, despite their scanty covering of hair, attempt to make the same adjustment. The contraction of the muscles in the skin raises the hairs and also produces little pits between them as "goose pimples" each surrounded by puckered skin.

At the same time that the tension of skeletal muscles increases, the heart beats a little faster. These activities add to the lactic acid in the blood and to the work of the liver. (The liver converts the lactic acid into six-carbon sugars by processes freeing additional heat into the circulating blood.)

If the animal continues to lose heat faster than the body is producing it, the muscular coats around arteries leading to the skin may contract, keeping the blood from the body surface and conserving the heat around internal organs. Simultaneously, the contractions of skeletal muscles may become spasmodic and uncontrollable. This is shivering, which produces still more heat.

When the outside temperature is high, the animal may have difficulty losing to the air all of the heat produced internally. Under these circumstances, the feathers or fur are allowed to lie flat, pressing out the air blanket next to the skin. The tension of skeletal muscles may be decreased, and the animal becoming unwilling to move from a prone position in the shade. Instinctively it will do as little muscular work as possible. The heartbeat slows down, and the glandular activity of internal organs decreases. Even digestion may be postponed. The muscular coats around arteries to the skin relax, too, and a larger part of the blood comes to the surface, where it can lose heat. This may make the skin conspicuously pink. Sweat glands in the skin pour out a watery secretion—its evaporation then cools the skin. Animals with few sweat glands usually pant. This action, seen in dogs, cats, and many birds, encourages evaporation of moisture from mouth and tongue. All these adjustments help keep the blood temperature constant.

Cold-blooded animals, by contrast, are rarely more than a degree or two warmer than their surroundings. Whenever the outside temperature falls, so does their body temperature; chemical activities in the body slow down markedly. A cold-blooded animal uses more energy when the temperature is high, whereas a warm-blooded animal uses extra energy to keep itself either warmer or cooler than its surroundings.

Chemical Coordination

In the first years of the twentieth century, scientists discovered that animals possess a chemical control system which regulates the millions of body cells, guiding this huge population to cooperate in a single individual. The chemical messages produced at one point in an animal, effective in other parts of the organization, are called hormones.

All cells in an individual are constantly producing minute amounts of chemical substances that travel to adjacent cells and keep activities there in step. Similarly, all cells constantly receive minute amounts of chemical substances to which they are sensitive. Responding to these, they adjust their own activities within the body. Vertebrate animals and arthropods show a special development of chemical coordination in that many hormones are produced in distinctive organs known as the endocrine organs or ductless glands. Each contributes its products only to the blood stream. Additional hormones are produced by special cells in organs that have another, quite different role in the animal.

The pituitary gland, the thyroid and parthyroid glands, and the adrenal glands are all distinct, specialized organs in vertebrate animals. Except for the production of specific hormones, they have no known role. Other hormones come from the wall cells of the stomach and small intestine, from the pancreas, from the ovaries and testes, and in female mammals, from membranes called the placenta, which are most important in nourishing the fetus. No doubt a great many other sources of hormones await discovery.

The thyroid gland, in the neck region, gathers in essentially all of the iodine obtained from food. The gland incorporates the iodine into the hormone thyroxine. Then, according to the chemical guidance received by the thyroid gland from the pituitary gland, the thyroxine is released into the blood stream to be carried to all parts of the body. In each cell it regulates the rate at which the carbohydrates are used in production of energy, including heat. Extra thyroxine leads to increased demands for oxygen, greater activity and heat production, and release of more carbon dioxide. Continued release of more thyroxine than normal causes an animal to be especially irritable and to lose weight. By contrast, an inadequate supply of the hormones lets the animal's rate of activity fall so low that the creature becomes sleepy, inattentive, and gains weight. It is unable to use all the energy it obtains in its food.

Insufficient iodine in the diet is often the cause of an inadequate supply of thyroxine in the blood. If this dietary deficiency occurs in childhood, a person's growth may be stunted seriously and mental abilities impaired; feebleminded dwarfs of this kind are called cretins. In later life, a similar lack of iodine in the diet is likely to bring about an abnormal growth of the thyroid gland, as though additional glandular tissue could produce more thyroxine. When the thyroid causes a bulge in the neck, a person is said to have simple goiter. In many parts of the world where food and water contain too little iodine, goiter formerly was common. Today, people have learned to use iodized table salt or to include iodine-containing seafoods in their diet to keep the thyroid gland properly supplied.

The spectacular transformation of a tadpole into a frog is controlled by the thyroid gland. Insufficient thyroxine leads to prolongation of the swimming stage, whereas an oversupply brings on early metamorphosis. Even a very young tadpole will reconstruct its body into adult form of miniature size within a few weeks if it is fed bits of thyroid gland tissue.

A hormone from the pituitary gland controls the activity of the thyroid gland. Under ordinary circumstances, the pituitary's output of thyroid-controlling hormone is adjusted according to the amount of thyroxine in the blood. As the thyroxine concentration in the blood plasma rises, the pituitary reduces its output of thyroid-stimulating hormone. When the thyroxine concentration falls, the pituitary responds by releasing more of the hormone, stimulating the thyroid to greater activity.

Many—perhaps all—of the hormone mechanisms in the body show this dual arrangement, through which a fairly steady output can be maintained. It is the living counterpart of the electronic circuits that engineers call a "feedback net-work." The most familiar example may be the automatic volume control of modern radios. It serves to keep the loud-speaker at a steady level of loudness in spite of variations in the strength of the signal picked up by the radio's antenna. In radio and hormone network alike, the outcome is a steady state. Nutrition, growth, excretion, maturation, and repro-duction are all managed by hormonal feedback systems. They provide control without endangering the continuity of the multicellular organism.

The parathyroid glands, which in mankind lie embedded in the thyroid, also interact with the pituitary in producing a hormone, one controlling the amount of calcium in the blood plasma. The adrenal glands, close to the kidneys, are sim-ilarly regulated; they elaborate a number of different chemi-cal messengers. Among these are substances necessary for the appearance and maintenance of those body features that show the sex of the individual—the "secondary sexual characters" such as a beard and deep voice in man. Adrenal hormones also include adrenalin, which affects the whole body's preparedness for emergencies, and cortisone, which is important in a wide variety of processes from maintenance of the joints of the skeleton to carbohydrate metabolism and the concentrations of both sodium and potassium com-pounds in the blood.

Insulin, the hormone regulating the conversion of blood sugar into glycogen to be stored in the liver and muscles, is produced by groups of cells scattered through much of the pancreas. These cells were described as "islets" about a century ago by the German pathologist Paul Langerhans, and are known as the "islets of Langerhans." They are en-tirely distinct from the gland cells that elaborate the digestive secretion of the pancreas.

The pituitary gland, lying between the brain and the roof of the mouth, produces an especially large number of dif-ferent hormones, many of them influencing the output of other endocrine organs. One of its hormones normally counterbalances the output of insulin, and maintains enough sugar in the blood that all cells of the body have this source of energy readily available. The balance is upset if the supply of insulin diminishes, producing the symptoms of diabetes: a rise in the concentration of sugar in the blood, until the kidneys excrete this valuable material; and depletion of the reserves of glycogen in the liver and muscles.

Another hormone produced by the pituitary gland stimulates the outer layer of the adrenal gland to secrete a different hormone—a substance almost indistinguishable from the synthetic compound called cortisone. The pituitary hormone with this effect has such a long name—adrenocorticotrophic hormone—that it is known more widely by its initials as ACTH. An inadequate supply of ACTH, indicating partial failure of this pituitary function, or an insufficient production of cortisone because of improper activity of the adrenals, may now be corrected by injection.

Nervous Coordination

To be active enough to escape from enemies and capture its own food, a multicellular animal needs a coordinating mechanism that acts more rapidly than hormones can. Every animal more complex than a sponge does possess such a mechanism. It consists of special cells in which the fundamental irritability of protoplasm is overdeveloped. Among coelenterates, such as hydras and jellyfishes, these special cells form a network with long extensions reaching to surface cells of both the outer and the inner body layers. In all other invertebrates and every vertebrate, they form a distinct nervous system with transmission lines (nerves) and control centers, each a ganglion or a brain. Often still other cells show special sensitivity to light or pressure or temperature change, and transmit any local excitation to the nervous system.

The basic unit of any nervous system is the nerve cell or neuron, which has the ability to transmit electrochemical changes from one end of itself to the other at a speed between 3 and 300 feet per second. These changes, called nerve impulses, are able to induce activity in other neurons, or to cause a gland to secrete, a muscle to contract, a luminescent organ to emit light.

Each neuron consists of a cell body, containing the nucleus and being the nutritive center, and at least one long slender extension (a nerve fiber) insulated from others by a sheath of fatty material. The one fiber is an axon, carrying excitation toward another neuron or a cell in a muscle or a gland that can respond. Additional fibers, called dendrites, may extend from the cell body and serve to pick up excitation. Nerve fibers running parallel to one another, like the wires in a telephone cable, constitute the nerves of the body.

In all vertebrate animals, the neurons work in teams, like the members of a relay racing team. Generally a team has three members, one a neuron associated with an especially sensitive receptor cell, a second carrying excitation from the first neuron to the third, and the third neuron linked to a muscle cell or a gland cell or some other "effector" cell. This simple team is called a reflex arc, and is the basis for many involuntary reactions of animals when some change in the environment is detected.

A reflex arc that is easy to demonstrate begins with specially sensitive receptor cells in the tendon of the human kneecap. If a person sits on a table with his legs over the side, only a light tap on the knee is needed to cause the lower leg to kick out involuntarily. Physicians often test this reaction, using a little rubber hammer to tap the knee during a physical examination.

When stimulated by the light blow, the receptor cells in the tendon induce the formation of nerve impulses in the associated dendrites of neurons whose cell bodies are far up the sciatic nerve, close to the spinal cord. From these cell bodies, short axons extend, carrying the nerve impulses into the spinal cord itself. There they stimulate the second neuron in each train to produce and conduct another set of impulses. These, in turn, affect the dendrites of the third neuron in each train, eliciting impulses in it that rush down a different nerve fiber in the sciatic nerve to a muscle cell in the thigh. In response to these messages, the muscles contract, extending the leg in the characteristic knee-jerk. A prompt reaction tells the physician that this level of the spinal cord and the sciatic nerves are operating properly.

Other examples of reflex arcs are those responsible for the withdrawal of a pricked finger, and the shutting of the eyelids when a twig from a tree threatens to strike the eyes. These reactions occur even when the person is expecting the prick, or knows that the eyes are protected by a heavy plate of glass. In each instance the reflex action is completed before the brain is made aware, through still other impulses in additional neurons, that the stimulus has been received.

No spark jumps across the microscopic gap between the tip of the axon from one neuron and the tip of the dendrite toward the next neuron in a reflex arc. Instead, the tip of the axon secretes a minute amount of a chemical substance to which the dendrite tip is sensitive. Each nerve impulse received at the axon tip induces a little secretion. At the same time, the tip of the dendrite produces a chemical compound that neutralizes the secretion. Only if several impulses arrive in a brief time may the amount of secretion be enough to induce the dendrite to send off new nerve impulses. Thus the chemical step in the passage of excitation from one neuron to the next limits it to one-way transmission. This chemical step is also the place where some poisons act. Strychnine alters the sensitivity of the dendrite tips until stimuli so mild that they normally would have no effect suddenly lead to convulsions.

Local anesthetics affect the receptor cells. Often they are highly selective. This is possible because the many unlike kinds of receptors are served by separate nerve fibers. Touch is distinct from pain, from temperature, from the various tastes and odors. Through the complex development of eyes and ears, light and sound are made meaningful to an animal.

Additional sensitive receptors monitor the internal activities of the body, whether the movement of food in the digestive tract or of blood in the circulatory system.

The central nervous system receives all of this information only in the form of nerve impulses. The message becomes meaningful according to which nerve fiber brings it, and according to a very simple code. Isolated nerve impulses, arriving no more frequently than one in each ⅕ second, may be ignored. Two may be enough to induce a sensation. Still more impulses arriving within the same brief time signify that the stimulus is stronger. With no more than this variation we identify the brighter of two lights differing in energy output by only six parts in a thousand, or tell the oboe from the French horn in listening to an orchestra. A firefly can find a mate of his own kind in the dark, a kingfisher can plunge for a fish below the surface of a stream, or a mother bat find the baby she left behind on the wall of a lightless cave.

It is the receptor cells in the eye and ear that determine the range of sensitivity through which they can be useful to the animal possessing them. Our eyes inform the brain about events in the surrounding scene, following them through a range of energy content greater than a billion to one—from landscape illuminated only by the stars in the night sky to a beach of white coral sand under a tropical sun at high noon. Human receptor cells respond to radiant energy from the far violet through the visible spectrum to deep red. They will detect also the near ultraviolet if the lens of the eye, which acts as a yellowish filter, is removed surgically. Most insects show great sensitivity to ultraviolet. Honeybees, at least, see this radiation invisible to us as a distinct color. Some fireflies can see farther than we into the red end of the spectrum, and will respond to infrared radiation to which our eyes are blind.

The sensitivity of sense organs changes with age. Our own eyes tells us progressively less of the violet end of the spectrum as we grow older, for the lens becomes more yellowish and filters out this part from our vision. At the same time, our ears grow less able to detect high-pitched notes. Most children can hear a whistle vibrating between 15,000 and 20,000 times a second; most older people cannot.

Human beings cannot detect a 24,000-cycle tone to which almost any dog's ears are sensitive. This is the pitch at which rats appear to communicate with one another. Both dogs and rats, however, are deaf of the echo-ranging calls of bats, in the vicinity of 40,000 to 80,000 vibrations per second, with which they track a flying insect or dodge branches in their path through the darkness.

An animal's response to stimuli from the surrounding world is often modified because of nerve impulses coming to the central nervous system from receptors in internal organs. A hungry rat will run great distances on an exercise wheel in its cage, and show in the speed of its running a crude indication of the severity of its hunger. Caterpillars of the brown-tailed moth *Euproctis* climb upward when hungry, downward when fed. This behavior takes them to the branch tips where the tenderest foliage awaits them, or the leaf litter on the ground where they are less exposed to insect-eating birds.

Combinations of external stimuli sometimes lead to different responses. The common water flea *Daphnia* is attracted strongly to light if the water around it is acid, whether from decaying vegetation or accumulation of carbon dioxide. If the acid is neutralized, it loses its response to light. Ordinarily these reactions lead it to the surface of a stagnant pond, where oxygen is more plentiful.

Unlearned behaviors of this kind depend upon a general type of stimulus, such as hunger or the condition of the environment or the concentration of some hormone; these stimuli "release" the behavior. But unless the second stimulus, such as light or gravity, is there to give activity a direction, nothing may happen. Most instinctive acts, depending upon a releasing stimulus and a directing stimulus, gain something for the animal under its normal living conditions.

An instinct consists of a chain of reflexes, all unlearned, in which the response to one reflex leads to the stimulus for another reflex. If a human baby is hungry, he cries; at first this is merely a reflex. If the crying causes something soft to come in contact with his cheek, he stops crying and turns his head to bring the soft object to his lips; this is a second reflex. If the soft object is a nipple around which his lips can close, he begins to suck; this is a third reflex. The whole chain is instinctive originally, a feature of any child's nervous system at birth.

The child, like many animals, learns quickly by experience. Often it is a matter of recognizing that some appetite (such as hunger) is satisfied under special circumstances, perhaps when a certain person arrives or a clock chimes a certain number of times. Soon the reflexes that are brought into use in satisfying the appetite may be set off by the unrelated stimulus. The classical example of such "conditioned responses" was a dog taught by the Russian physiologist Ivan Pavlov. It learned to associate the sound of a bell or the light of an electric lamp with the arrival of food. Soon it would drool if the bell rang or the lamp was turned on, even when no food appeared.

Rats learn to run a maze from the release box to some reward. Or a cat learns to pull and push levers in a particular sequence as the means to escape from confinement. They are profiting from experience during a period of purely trial-and-error behavior. This is called "instrumental learning." Some animals will go a step farther, and identify some general feature of the experimental conditions, such as turning right every third division of the route, or pulling on alternate levers. Theirs is "perceptual learning." Often it corresponds to a slight hesitation before each choice, as though the animal were mentally weighing the alternatives before relying upon its insight as to the rule it must follow.

Instincts are particularly valuable to small, short-lived creatures that have no time for learning. Insects and most other arthropods are primarily instinctive in their behavior.

Learning and various indications of intelligence, such as insight, become more valuable in animals with longer lives. They have opportunity to learn by observing other individuals, or through personal trial-and-error or trial-and-success.

A hungry spider has no time to waste in learning to spin a web. Nor can a bird delay in building a nest in spring. These actions depend entirely upon instincts. But a monkey in a tree gains considerably by looking for alternate routes through the jungle and choosing one, or in deciding just which is the next limb to be jumped to. Some time spent in contemplation can save its life. This seems to be particularly true for animals that live above the ground. Insight and intelligence appear easier to find among the longer-lived denizens of trees, such as the monkeys and apes and their heavier relatives upon the ground, man.

CHAPTER
5

How Animals Reproduce

A clear proof of genius appeared in the year 1651 on the decorated title page of a treatise on embryology. The illustration shows Jove enthroned, opening an egg that is a veritable Pandora's box. Out of the gap in the shell spill a child, a stag, a bird, a lizard, a snake, a fish, a grasshopper, a butterfly, a spider, and some plants. Upon the shell is lettered EX OVO OMNIA—"all come from an egg." This was William Harvey's prediction, going much farther than anyone knew at the time. He was the same man who, over twenty years earlier, had announced that blood circulates through the human heart. Harvey's mind had lost none of its power.

Except for those animals and plants that arise as individuals from a separated part of a previous animal or plant, every living thing does come from an egg. An egg, in fact, is an amazing single cell containing all of the guidance needed to produce a new multicellular individual in close likeness to the parent or parents. At the same time it contains all of the food materials the developing animal will need until it reaches additional supplies from outside the egg.

The eggs of most animals must be fertilized if they are to develop into new individuals. This implies that a sperm cell, from among millions contributed by the father, fuses with the egg cell readied by the mother. The nucleus of the sperm cell contributes the inheritable characteristics of the father, and adds these to a similar set included in the unfertilized egg by the mother. These halves of the joint heritage, one half from the father and one half from the mother, remain combined. They are duplicated completely and then parceled out when the one-celled fertilized egg divides to become a two-celled embryo. This reduplication (called replication) and division of the nucleus is completed again before each of the two cells divides, producing a four-celled embryo. Over and over this process is repeated, providing every cell of the new individual with a complete heritage representing both parental lines.

The inheritance in the nucleus of a fertilized egg is organized in so limited a space that it gives no obvious character to the egg of any one species, when the egg is considered as a whole. The distinguishing features of an egg lie, instead, in the amount and kind of food it holds for the embryo, and in its protective features such as a surrounding jelly or a shell. The egg of a sea star is about $\frac{1}{200}$ inch in diameter and contains little nourishment. Usually it is discharged into the open ocean, there to develop for a few days into a strange little larva that can transform into a minute sea star and begin browsing on miscroscopic plants, digesting them in its alimentary canal.

A human egg is scarcely larger, and about equal in size to the egg of a mouse, a whale, or an elephant. All of these tiny eggs of mammals depend upon a new supply of nourishment to be obtained from the mother as the embryo progresses toward birth. A frog's egg, by contrast, may be $\frac{1}{16}$ inch in diameter, and contain granules of yolk sufficing to feed the developing embryo from one to three weeks, depending on the coolness of the water. At the end of this time the tadpole must be ready to emerge from the protective jelly into the pond, where it can find single-celled plants as food. Months of growth still lie ahead of it before it can transform into a small frog recognizably like its parents.

The egg of a reptile or bird encloses within its shell not only enough yolk for a far longer period of rapid development, but also a dilute albumen that takes the place of a pond, supplying the embryo with water and space for growth and movement. Today the largest of these eggs is the three-pound product of the African ostrich, equivalent in volume to two dozen large-sized eggs of the domestic hen. The extra nourishment it contains lasts a larger chick for forty days of incubation—twice as long as for eggs of the domestic fowl.

When allowances are made for the degree to which the stores of food get in the way of the developing embryo, it is evident that the eggs of sea star, mouse, man, elephant, frog, fish, fence lizard, and domestic fowl all go through closely similar steps in early development. In each the initial cell of the fertilized egg becomes divided into a multitude; these cells rearrange themselves in a single layer around a cavity (the blastocoel). One wall of this cavity folds inward, largely obliterating the blastocoel but at the same time creating a new pocket of greater significance. Slowly the pocket closes off from the outside world as the hollow beginning of the digestive tube. Around it are cells (endoderm tissue) that will become the lining of the alimentary canal. They are distinct from cells (ectoderm tissue) left covering the outside of the embryo.

Further steps in a vertebrate embryo utilize some of the ectodermal cells toward formation of a hollow dorsal tube that bulges at its anterior end at the beginnings of brain and spinal cord. Where ectoderm and endoderm appear to meet around the opening connecting the digestive pocket to the outside world, the cells have even greater significance. They begin multiplying and moving into the remains of the blastocoel, there to become organized as the many products of the third "germ layer" of the embryo—the mesoderm.

The ectoderm eventually furnishes the outer layer (epidermis) of the skin, the complete nervous system and pituitary gland, the retina and the lens of the eyes, and part or all of scales, nails, claws, hoofs, teeth, antlers, horns, hair, and feathers. The endoderm becomes the lining of the digestive tract and of its big digestive glands (the liver and pancreas), the pancreatic islets of Langerhans, the lining of the lungs, and of the urinary bladder, as well as the thyroid and the parathyroid glands. The remainder of the body is of mesodermal origin: the dermis of the skin, including part of all true horns and teeth; the remainder of the eyes and of the liver and pancreas; all of the skeleton and muscles; all of the circulatory system, including the blood; the entire excretory and reproductive systems; and most of the endocrine glands.

In every instance, the embryo first blocks out the major body parts, and then refines the details in each. A general mass is destined to become nervous system before it shows any indication of the limits of brain and spinal cord; nerves arise later. Head and tail become recognizably distinct from the body, and limbs then appear as lumps ("buds") that, for a time, lack any indication as to whether they will be arms rather than legs or wings or the flippers of a seal. The circulatory system arises as a tube looped upon itself, and one broadened part begins to beat as an effective heart before the organ is committed to becoming the two-chambered organ of a cyclostome or fish, the three-chambered heart of an amphibian or lizard, or the four-chambered pump of a warm-blooded creature. Only gradually does an embryo reveal the final form that alone will match the heritage carried in its nuclei.

The human embryo uses its first eighteen days of existence to organize right and left, with a slight neck indicating the limits of head and trunk, but with little to show where body ends and tail begins. It has reached a length of $\frac{1}{20}$ of an inch; at this stage almost three-quarters of the embryo is destined to become head. The trunk grows much more rapidly thereafter.

At three weeks of age, the human embryo has deep grooves

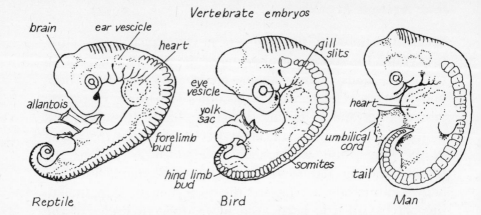

Vertebrate embryos

brain — ear vescicle — heart — gill slits — eye vesicle — allantois — yolk sac — heart — forelimb bud — umbilical cord — hind limb bud — somites — tail

Reptile   Bird   Man

on the sides of the neck, as though it were preparing for gills useful in aquatic life. The growing heart forms a great bulge high in the chest region. The tail is very obvious. By the fourth week the heart is beating, the blood circulating, but the gill grooves are disappearing. The globes of the eyes have begun to appear. At five weeks the limb buds extend, with no indication of subdivisions. The tail is short and stubby. In another week the limbs will end in toes or fingers which can be counted, although they will differ little in shape from the corresponding features on the embryo of a cat or an elephant.

The human embryo begins to respond to stimuli at eight weeks, indicating that the nervous system has made its connections with sensitive cells in the skin and with muscles. The muscles too are ready to contract. By then the embryo is recognizably human and is called a fetus. During the twelfth week, a variety of muscle reactions appear, most of them involving the whole body. The hands turn until the palms face each other. The organs of balance in the inner ear have reached full size, and the eyeballs are performing roving movements under the eyelids, although these are still fused together.

At twenty weeks—halfway through a normal period of gestation—the human fetus is about eight inches long and weighs about a pound. Yet, for another five weeks it cannot maintain the breathing movements necessary for life in air longer than a few minutes or hours. The critical week is the twenty-eighth, at the end of which a premature baby can be expected to survive in an incubator. At this stage it will show no awareness of its surroundings, and seems to be in a state part way between sleep and wakefulness. Its eyes open and the eyeballs turn in various directions without responding to any moving object. The muscles of the face contract from time to time, giving the fetus a wide range of meaningless expressions.

Awareness, even though brief, appears at the thirty-fourth week—six weeks before full term—and the eyes may follow irregularly after objects that move. Until the thirty-eighth week, however, sleep and wakefulness are barely distinguishable, and the infant has not yet built up the fat deposits that round out the body outline.

The marvel is that so much of the final body organization is in workable condition as early as the twenty-eighth week, although it may not be called upon until the forty-fourth week. Yet, given a few minutes notice, the human infant is ready to emerge from a temperature-controlled aquarium inside the mother and begin breathing its own air, excreting its own nitrogenous wastes, controlling its own body temperature (within limits), and screaming for something to eat—as well as digesting its own meals. These activities require drastic changes in the routes taken by the blood, and the use of a whole array of organs that have been completed but kept as stand-bys: the lungs, kidneys, digestive tract, and vocal cords.

The organization of a human infant is far from complete at the time of normal birth. Use of both eyes at once while examining an object does not come until the second month after a full-term birth. A month more may be needed before the eyes begin to follow the hands and feet. Walking alone is an accomplishment of the fourteenth month on the average, and is a measure of the progressing development of the nervous system rather than opportunity or training. A child that has been kept immobilized on an Indian-style cradle board will walk just as soon and as well as the infant whose parents have been giving it freedom and encouragement.

Young mammals differ tremendously from one kind to another in the degree to which they are ready to fend for themselves at birth. The colt staggers awkwardly after its mother within fifteen minutes. A newborn antelope will do its best—running at perhaps fifteen miles per hour—to keep up with the herd long before its coat is dry. A young porcupine will raise its quills and attempt to defend itself within seconds after being born, and weans itself—wandering off on its own—at a very tender age.

The same can be seen among birds. The chick of the domestic fowl scurries around, picking up food, within a few minutes after hatching. A pigeon squab depends upon food regurgitated by its parents until, at an age of about six weeks, it molts for the first time and acquires feathers useful in flight. Young European starlings and American robins follow their parents about, begging for food, long after they have reached adult size and the ability to fly expertly. Each kind of animal has its own schedule, determining when the young can be independent.

This schedule includes also the age at which an animal becomes sexually mature: a mouse or a rat at two months after birth; a domestic pig at four months; a bat and a deer at twelve; a cow at eighteen; a great blue whale at three years; a sockeye salmon from four to eight years; an Indian elephant between eight and eleven years; and a loggerhead turtle at a still greater age.

Provision for the Young

Parental care is beyond prediction. Almost every group of multicellular animals above the level of sponges includes at least a few in which the mother or father provides to some extent for the young, as though recognizing a responsibility there. Often this care ceases after the mother has placed her eggs where they will be concealed from enemies.

Most sea stars cast their eggs into the sea at random, but a few—particularly in arctic and antarctic seas—retain the eggs until the young emerge, and provide brood pouches in which the little stars are fairly safe until they grow large enough to fend for themselves. Squids affix to the sea bottom banana-shaped masses of jelly containing numerous eggs, leaving these "dead men's fingers" protected only by some chemical compound that makes them bad tasting, if not actually poisonous. The closely related octopus, however, stands guard over her eggs, and polishes them with her sucker-studded tentacles. Or she hoses them clean with a jet of water from her breathing cavity, staying in constant attendance for as much as three months without even taking off time for a meal.

The African korper fish *Tillapia* is a mouth-brooder, that picks up the eggs in a capacious mouth and protects them there until they hatch. Sea horses have a very different method: the male wears a brood pouch, and opens it as a cavity into which his mate will lay her eggs. He swims about with the embryos, and releases them one at a time only after each has become a miniature version of himself. Nor is this the most a fish is known to do for its young. As Aristotle discovered several centuries before the beginning of the Christian Era, the dogfish shark of the Mediterranean Sea develops an intimate connection between mother and unborn young—a placenta very much like those of mammals, in which the blood of the developing youngster can come so near the blood stream of the mother that it can receive nourishment and oxygen from her and get rid of carbon dioxide and dissolved wastes.

We human beings tend to regard a placenta as a sort of trademark, and its relic on our abdominal wall—the umbilicus or navel, where the umbilical cord connected us to the placenta—as something unique to man and warm-blooded animals with hair. But quite an assortment of other types among the cold-blooded animals also develop a structure similar to a placenta. Some of the sharks and scorpions

are so equipped, and a few kinds of wormlike peripatus as
well.

The distinction between an egg-laying and a live-bearing
creature is less than might be thought. The common little
horned lizards *Phrynosoma* of Texas dig a nest in which to
lay a dozen eggs or so. Their nearest kin—members of the
same genus in New Mexico and Arizona—bring forth active
young instead. During the later part of development the
blood-carrying membranes which surround the embryo of
all reptiles, birds, and mammals may serve to pick up oxygen
and dispose of carbon dioxide through the shell of the egg,
or attend to this same exchange inside the oviduct of the
mother.

Most scorpions lay eggs under a stone or a board and
then stand guard over them until they hatch. The young
customarily climb upon the mother's back and ride along
with her for several days. By dropping off one at a time they
take advantage of her longer legs in getting distributed widely
over the terrain. Wolf spiders deposit their eggs into silken
sacs as much as ¾ of an inch in diameter, and carry the
egg ball tied on behind; newly hatched young often cling to
the parent's abdomen for a week or more. By contrast, the
house spider and the black widow spider stand guard beside
their irregular egg bags, hung in a corner of the loosely constructed nest. Black widows are most likely to bite when de-
fending the nest from invaders, often human beings on a
quite unrelated errand.

The care and nourishment given by mammals and birds
to their young are so well known that it is easy to overlook
similar behavior among the less conspicuous animals. Yet
each of the 660,000 different kinds of insects has its own
way of handling its eggs. Often the type of parental care provides an interesting insight into the insect's way of life. The
mother cockroach, for example, produces a flat purse-shaped
packet of eggs and carries it about with her until they are
nearly ready to hatch. Then she drops it somewhere, usually
in a crevice, and pays no attention to the young that emerge,

each of them a junior version of herself, although lacking the wings that only adult insects ever possess.

Grasshoppers and crickets conceal their eggs in the soil. Sometimes so many choose the same small area of level ground as a hiding place for eggs that a mouse or skunk detects the buried treasure of nourishment and digs them out. Katydids cement their eggs to a branch, each egg tucked under the edge of the preceding one until they overlap like shingles. Praying mantises stand head downward on twigs and whip up a meringuelike foam around each egg cluster; the material hardens quickly and protects the eggs through the winter. Stick insects merely drop their eggs singly wherever they happen to be standing; each egg bounces from leaf to leaf and to the ground, rattling like a pellet of lead shot.

Tumble bugs are beetles that lay their eggs on balls of dung which they have rolled to a suitable bit of soil and buried there. The sacred scarab of Egypt has this interesting habit. The ancients saw it as a symbol of the gods rolling the ball of the sun across the sky from dawn until dusk, and pointed to details of the beetle's anatomy as indicating the

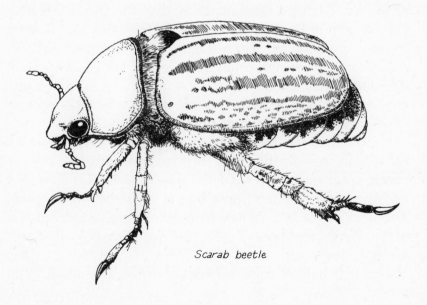

Scarab beetle

number of days in a week, the rays of the sun, and other features of mystical importance.

Ordinarily a pair of tumble bugs cooperate in rolling and burying the dung ball. The female remains only long enough to lay her egg on the buried store of food. The grub which emerges from the egg resembles the C-shaped young of a May beetle and, like it, feeds until a resting stage is reached. While lying motionless, the insect transforms from the grub stage to a pupa, and then to adult form. The pupa of a beetle corresponds to the bullhead stage of a mosquito, to the chrysalis stage of a butterfly, and to the enclosed animal within a moth's silken cocoon.

For the male tumble bug to show instinctive concern for the ball of dung that will provide his offspring with food is a mark of social progress among insects. Sexton beetles go another step. After a pair of them have buried a dead mouse or other small carcass as food for the young, the adults remain with the eggs until they hatch and feed the maggot-like larvae for a time by regurgitation.

The social insects, which include the termites ("white ants"), true ants, and social bees, as well as some wasps, show still greater organization into communities of cooperating individuals. Termites are unique in that the immature individuals help in the work of the colony, cleaning and feeding younger brothers and sisters. Like some of the true ants and social bees, the termites may include in each colony several different castes, each with its special role. Food gathering, civil defense, and reproduction are likely to be tasks each of which is attended to by a distinct caste of individuals.

A great deal has been learned about the ways of domesticated honeybees as they tend their exceptionally helpless offspring in artificial hives. Of the 60,000 to 80,000 bees in a beehive at midsummer, only one is a mother—the queen. The work of the hive is done by unmarriageable older sisters of the developing bees, leaving the queen to be a specialist at egg-laying.

The first half of each worker's six-week life as an adult

is spent inside the hive, following a remarkable schedule that leads her from one task to another.

For the first three days, the worker spends hours cleaning herself and begging food from older bees. Her only work seems to be cleaning the new cells in the brood comb, putting a varnish of saliva all around the inner surface. The queen bee will not lay an egg in a cell of the brood comb until this varnish has been applied.

After these three days, the young worker finds her way to the storage cells of the hive and begins to eat honey and pollen from them. Some of this food she regurgitates to the oldest larvae, but most of it goes toward the growth of special glands in the throat region of her digestive tract—close to the mouth. By the fifth or sixth day, these glands begin to secrete a highly nutritious, nitrogen-rich "brood food." The worker then shifts her attention to doling out this secretion to the youngest larvae. She continues in these duties until she is twelve or thirteen days into adulthood, at which time her supply of brood food decreases and the wax glands below her abdomen become active. For the next six days she uses the wax in fashioning comb within the hive, leaving the welfare of the larvae to workers younger than herself.

As a worker's wax supply gives out, it becomes time for the bee to go to the door of the hive. Her new duties include relieving incoming field bees of their loads of nectar and pollen, storing these treasures in their proper cells, removing dead bees or other debris from the hive, fanning with her wings to create a ventilating current of air into the hive, and guarding the door to keep out foreign insects.

The worker bee has been an adult for three weeks before she tries out her wings in flight, and learns the location of the hive in relation to landmarks. It is six weeks since she was just a new-laid egg, for the first three weeks of her existence were needed for development inside the egg, next as a larva, and then through the pupal transformation. Now she is ready to go collecting food in the field, on trip after trip until her wings are frayed with wear.

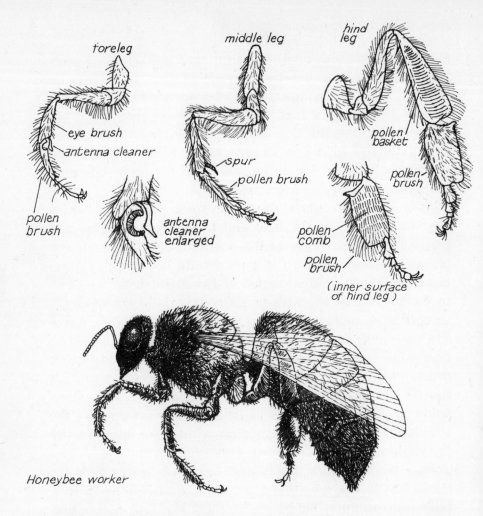

foreleg

middle leg

hind leg

eye brush

antenna cleaner

pollen brush

antenna cleaner enlarged

spur

pollen brush

pollen basket

pollen brush

pollen comb

pollen brush

(inner surface of hind leg)

Honeybee worker

The only members of the hive who do no work are the big-eyed drones (males), a few hundred of which may be fed from the precious stores of honey to keep them ready for the day when a new queen will emerge for her marriage flights. After that day, the drones are thrust from the hive and let starve to death.

Part of the colonial organization that provides such systematic care for the young bees is a code by means of which workers returning from the field with food can communicate to others in the hive a reliable indication of where additional supplies of food should be sought. This communication occurs in the darkness of the hive, but scientists have watched the procedure many times through deep red panes of glass which admit no light a bee can see To be sure what the messages meant, the bee-watchers have concentrated their attention on bees marked with a daub of paint—a mark applied when a particular worker discovered and took a load of sugar water from a dish some distance from the hive.

When a worker returns and mingles with other bees in the entranceway of the hive, she does not immediately give up her load of imitation nectar to waiting sisters. Instead, she first performs a little dance on the vertical surface of the comb. Other workers crowd around and learn by the way the dancer nudges them in the darkness the message she conveys.

No one knows yet how the workers assess the resources inside the hive and communicate this information to each other and to the queen bee. Yet when the store of honey and pollen reaches some measure of adequacy, the workers add new, large, almost vertical chambers among the brood comb. In these, new queens will develop from ordinary larvae fed a special diet rich in fats, proteins, and vitamins from pollen.

The day when a new queen is about to emerge from one of these special cells becomes known inside the hive, too. The worker bees grow excited and the pitch of their humming changes. The old queen ceases her egg laying, gathers a large part of the population of worker bees about her, and departs to found a new home. After the swarm has left, the new queen can inherit the hive. First she stings to death all of her unemerged competitors. Then she begins a few days of nuptial flights during which one drone after another succeeds in adding to the young queen's lifetime store of sperm cells. Finally she returns to the hive and settles down as the sole reproducing survivor of her generation.

In this social organization providing detailed care for the young, division of labor approaches the ultimate. The whole colony exists merely to promote the welfare of the queen's eggs. Only the exceptional individual of either sex has the possibility of reproducing. In a butterfly or a human being, by contrast, each individual retains the ability to reproduce new individuals, even though this function concerns a relatively small number of cells—the eggs or sperm. The rest of the butterfly, man, or woman is like a worker bee, with a definite life span and a responsibility in insuring that those eggs or sperm will contribute toward new generations for the future. As some wit remarked: "A hen is an egg's way of making another egg." The same applies to most animals and to the entire colony in a beehive.

CHAPTER
6

How Animals Inherit

Far back before the dawn of written history, mankind began to cultivate useful plants and to raise animals in captivity. Individual plants were chosen for propagation according to the size of their fruits or the vigor with which they grew. Animals selected for breeding were those that laid the biggest and most eggs or produced the most meat. Gradually, the domesticated plants and animals changed from their wild ancestors. Yet no one understood how heredity operated.

How much did the characteristics of each plant or animal depend upon its environment (its "nurture"), and how much on its inheritance (its "nature")? Even after the microscope was invented and sperm cells were discovered, the importance of the father's contribution to his offspring remained a mystery.

The first direct clue to the role of the male came in 1902, when C. E. McClung in Kansas discovered a visible difference between the cells in the body of male and female grasshoppers. In a female's body each cell contains a spherical nucleus with an even number of threadlike parts called chromosomes—two each of every different shape and length. In males, all except one pair matched up perfectly; the exceptional pair consisted of a large chromosome and a small one. McClung named the large one an X-chromosome and the small one a Y-chromosome.

Among the chromosomes in body cells of female grasshoppers, McClung could see one pair that seemed to match in size and shape the X-chromosomes of male grasshoppers. He made an intelligent guess at the explanation. Perhaps any individual whose body cells contained two of the X-chromosomes was a female, and any individual whose body cells contained one X-chromosome and one Y-chromosome was a male. He called the X- and Y-chromosomes "sex chromosomes" while pointing out how simply the sex of an individual might be inherited in this way.

Today we know that McClung had the right idea. Each human body cell similarly contains twenty-three different pairs of chromosomes. In a man, these are an X-chromosome, a Y-chromosome, and twenty-two other pairs (called autosomes). In a woman, the nucleus in each body cell contains a pair of X-chromosomes and twenty-two pairs of autosomes.

When reproductive cells are being formed, a special type of division (called meiosis) parcels out the chromosomes in such a way that every egg cell gets one chromosome of each different kind. A human egg contains a nucleus with exactly twenty-three chromosomes, all different; twenty-two are autosomes and one is an X-chromosome. Similarly, every sperm cell receives a chromosome of each different kind. A human sperm contains a nucleus with twenty-two autosomes and one sex chromosome. The sex chromosome in the sperm has an equal chance of being an X-chromosome or a Y-chromosome. In any large number of sperm cells, half will contain an X-chromosome and half a Y-chromosome.

At fertilization, when a sperm cell joins an egg cell, the chromosomes in the nucleus of the sperm are added to those already in the nucleus of the egg. One complete set of chromosomes from each parent is thus combined to form a double set—two of each different chromosome—in the nucleus of the fertilized egg. Every time the cell divides in the development of an embryo and the growth of a new individual, each chromosome is duplicated exactly. In this way every body cell contains a nucleus with the same double set of chromosomes as the fertilized egg from which it grew.

If a sperm with an X-chromosome fertilizes an egg with an X-chromosome, the fertilized egg will have two X-chromosomes and the embryo will become a female. On the other hand, if a sperm with a Y-chromosome fuses with an egg with an X-chromosome, the combination XY is produced; from this fertilized egg a male will develop. Sex is determined at the moment of fertilization. Chance alone decides whether the egg will be fertilized by an X-bearing or a Y-bearing sperm. For this reason, the number of boys born is approximately equal to the number of girls born.

In the science of heredity, symbols are used to represent the inheritance of individuals. A boy or a man (or a male grasshopper) would be shown by the symbols XY, a girl or a woman (or a female grasshopper) by the symbols XX. A single letter, X or Y, would represent a reproductive cell. Only sperm cells can carry Y-chromosomes. All eggs are X.

Many inheritable characteristics are borne by each chromosome. Inability to distinguish red from green is a defect in human vision carried by the X-chromosome in some people. Any boy or man with this defect in the sole X-chromosome in each of his body cells is said to be color-blind, whereas a girl or woman must have this defect in *both* of her X-chromosomes in each body cell to be aware of any difficulty.

If a girl or woman has this defect in only one of the X-chromosomes in each body cell, her vision is as colorful as a normal man or woman, but her children may be afflicted. About 4 per cent of the male white population in America shows this type of color-blindness, but less than one per cent of the corresponding women fail to distinguish red from green. Their extra X-chromosomes save them.

The geneticist is very much interested in the inheritance of all kinds of characteristics, and uses his symbols to represent them in a way he can visualize easily. He knows now that there are only two types of human males in terms of red-green color vision, and indicates them as

X^cY a normal male, with color vision;

X^eY a red-green color-blind male.

But there are three different genetic constitutions of human females, shown as

X^cX^c a normal female, with color vision and no concealed color-blindness;

X^cX^e a female with color vision who "carries" color-blindness;

X^eX^e a red-green color-blind female.

If a red-green color-blind woman marries a normal man, all her sons will receive an X^e-chromosome from the mother, a Y-chromosome from the father, and be color-blind. All her daughters will receive an X^c-chromosome from the father and an X^e-chromosome from the mother, and have normal color vision but be "carriers."

Five other combinations of parents can be considered. One of them, X^cY with X^cX^c, will give rise only to children with normal color vision. Another combination, X^eY with X^eX^e, will give rise only to children unable to distinguish red from green. The outcome in each instance is easier to work out than any crossword puzzle.

The fact that a person who is X^cX^e can distinguish red from green shows that X^c can conceal the presence of the defect in the other sex chromosome. The normal type of vision is said to be "dominant" over this type of color-blindness, or the red-green color-blindness to be "recessive" to normal vision. These terms are also used in connection with other inheritable characteristics.

Until some individual can be examined who is known to have ancestors one line of which were completely normal and the other of which were equally abnormal for the characteristic, there is no way to predict whether the defect or the normal condition will be the dominant one. In human heredity, the abnormality of the hand known as "lobster claw" is a dominant, whereas red hair proves to be a recessive.

The chromosomes controlling color-vision and red-green color-blindess are represented in every cell of the body. Yet they have their effect only within the cells of the retina in the eye. The sex chromosomes similarly are present in every body cell, yet their influence in inducing development of sexual characteristics is very limited. Actually the sex chromosomes affect chiefly the pituitary and adrenal glands, and influence the hormones they secrete. The hormones, in turn, influence the mesodermal tissues, leading cells in a developing embryo to become ovaries—the organs in which eggs eventually will form—or to become testes, from which sperm cells will arise.

Occasionally, when a baby is born, it shows features of both sexes and the physician is uncertain whether its heredity is that of a girl or a boy. Recently a way has been found to learn the answer through examining the chromosomal material in a small sample of skin. The difference between XX and XY is evident there, and the physician can prescribe the correct treatment with hormones to help the individual develop fully the sex called for by the sex chromosomes.

Most inheritable characteristics express themselves more directly than those related to reproduction. They are carried on the "other" chromosomes (the autosomes) and not on the sex chromosomes. Yet the special division that parcels out one complete set of chromosomes to each egg cell or each sperm cell is responsible also for a random distribution of those inheritable features that bear no close dependence upon sex.

One of the more obvious differences among human beings, due to a feature carried in one of the autosomes, is the ability to curl the tongue. If a marriage combines two parental lines, one a family among which for several generations no member has been able to curl the tongue, and the other from a family all members of which have this amusing ability, a good prediction can be made: none of the children will be able to curl the tongue. This is merely relying upon experience that shows the ability to curl the tongue to be a recessive characteristic. The noncurling children, however, will carry the inheritance of the curling ancestors. They can be represented by the symbols Nn, where NN signifies the "pure line" of noncurling ancestors and the nn the pure line of curling ancestors.

If two people with the genetic make-up represented by Nn marry and have children, new combinations can arise. The husband provides two types of sperm cells, those carrying N in one of the autosomes, and those with n. Similarly, the wife produces two types of eggs in equal numbers: those with N, and those with n. If an N-carrying sperm fuses with an N-carrying egg, the offspring will be a non-curler with no hidden recessive characteristic. If an n-carrying sperm fuses with an n-carrying egg, the child will be able to curl the tongue and will have the genetic constitution nn. But if an N-carrying sperm fuses with an n-carrying egg, or if an n-carrying sperm fuses with an N-carrying egg, the offspring will be noncurlers concealing a recessive n. When the statistics from many families of this kind are combined, it is evident that on the average a family of four children will include one curler and three noncurlers. Yet only one of the noncurlers will have the genetic constitution NN, just like a pure-line noncurler. The others will be hybrids, represented by Nn, like the parents.

These relationships are easier to demonstrate in domestic animals than among human beings, because matings can be arranged and larger numbers of offspring studied. Among guinea pigs, for example, the young from a cross of a pure line of black guinea pigs and a pure line of white guinea pigs turn out all to be black. Black is dominant to white in guinea-pig coat color. Yet the white characteristic is not lost; it is merely hidden. If a pair of these black young is allowed to mature and mate, the next generation will include both white and black guinea pigs. If large numbers of this second generation are counted, the proportion is found to be three blacks to one white. Of each three blacks, on the average, one will be a pure-line individual concealing no recessive for white coat color.

The animal breeder uses the capital letter to represent dominant characteristics and the lower case letter for recessives. In the guinea pig example, he would indicate a pure-line black guinea pig as BB, and realize that every sperm cell or egg cell from such an individual would carry one chromosome containing the dominant B. Similarly a pure-line white guinea pig would be shown by bb, and the sex cells from such a guinea pig would include one chromosome carrying the recessive b. Any mating between BB and bb would combine a sperm and an egg bringing B together with b, starting off a new individual with the genetic make-up Bb —with black coat but carrying the recessive b in every cell of the body.

Hybrid individuals of constitution Bb form two kinds of sex cells: some with B, some with b. The number of B-carrying sex cells is equal to the number of b-carrying sex cells. In any mating between two Bb individuals, the chances are equally good for each of the four combinations possible: B with B, B with b, b with B, and b with b. Only the last combination gives rise to an individual with a white coat.

Geneticists have found guinea pigs to be useful animals for the study of inheritance. They become sexually mature about four months after birth, require just over two months of pregnancy to bring forth a litter of from four to twelve young, and will mate again immediately through a life span extending as much as eight years. Under ideal conditions, a single newborn pair of guinea pigs can have 4,702 descendants in two years, and be themselves but a quarter of their way along toward old age. Of the 4,704 animals at the end of twenty-four months, in fact, only 980 would be sexually mature. The combined litters born at twenty-six months from the beginning of the experiment could include 5,880 additional young.

In breeding experiments, only a small number of the possible offspring are permitted to survive. Even so, the space and food requirements for these studies become inconvenient, and the two-month delay between litters of guinea pigs or the four-month wait for sexual maturity may seem wasteful. Since almost all animals follow a single pattern in inheritance, time can be gained and costs cut by using smaller creatures with a shorter life history and more modest food requirements.

Geneticists have found the little fruit fly *Drosophila melanogaster* almost ideal in these respects. A pair that is given access to suitable food for their young can raise a family of about 200 additional flies in eleven days. If these are given similar opportunities, the next generation—at barely more than three weeks from the beginning of the experiment—can include 200,000 newly mature individuals!

In *Drosophila,* the normal red color of the eyes is a dominant characteristic carried on the X-chromosome. The recessive condition is white eyes. This is inherited in exactly the same way as red-green color-blindness in human beings, or as hemophilia. In fruit flies, a serious deformity of the wings (described as "vestigial" wings) is a recessive characteristic carried in an autosome, and transmitted from one generation to the next in a manner corresponding exactly to curling of the tongue in mankind or to white coat color in guinea pigs.

Not all inherited characteristics follow a simple pattern of dominance or recessiveness. In domestic cattle, for example, a pure line of red animals crossed with a pure line of white animals yields calves that are "roan," with both red hairs and white hairs in the coat, and obviously unlike either parent.

Their genetic constitution could be represented as Rr; they show "blending" inheritance.

In human beings the color of the skin depends upon at least two different inheritable characteristics showing blending. These might be indicated as SS and TT (written SSTT) for a full-blooded Negro, and sstt for a white. Then SSTt and SsTT would indicate a person with a very dark, but not black skin. The symbols SStt, SsTt, and ssTT would all correspond to medium brown skins, whereas Sstt and ssTt would match people with very light brown skins.

From this information, a person should be able to predict that, in a marriage between a Negro (SSTT) and a white person (sstt), the one parent would contribute one S and one T, the other parent an s and a t, giving the mulatto child the genetic make-up SsTt and a medium brown skin. A mulatto, on the other hand, passes on these determiners for skin color two at a time in four different combinations: ST, St, sT and st. In a mating between a mulatto and a white person, three different skin colors could be expected among the children: medium brown (SsTt), light brown (Sstt and ssTt), and white (sstt). The light brown children would be called quadroons (from the Spanish *cuarto*, meaning "quarter"), yet all of the offspring from this mating would have three white grandparents and one Negro grandparent. If the hair type and features of nose and lips in these quadroons showed the same blending inheritance with a strong tendency toward those of the white grandparents, they might easily be confused with well-tanned white children.

No scientific evidence supports the widely held idea that a black-skinned child can come from a marriage of a white and a mulatto. If one of the parents is white—truly white skinned—the children will not be darker than the parent of mixed racial ancestry. A darker child is possible, however, if both parents are part Negro. In a marriage between two mulattos, the children can be expected to include the full range of skin colors from black to white. On the average, one in sixteen offspring would be expected to have a black skin, one in sixteen a white skin, four in sixteen a dark brown skin, four in sixteen a light brown skin, and the remaining six a medium brown like that of their parents. The children of mulatto parents are known to be extremely variable.

Blood Groups

We speak of a "full-blooded" Indian or Negro as though the blood made the differences in skin color and facial features. Clearly this is not so. Yet the blood groups important in transfusions do follow a genetic pattern of their own. In this, the differences are in substances carried by the red blood cells and by the plasma. In blood group A, the red cells contain a material called antigen A. People of blood group B are so named because their red cells contain antigen B. Group AB people have both antigen A and antigen B in their red cells. Group O is characterized by the lack of both antigen A and antigen B in the red cells.

An antigen is a substance that, in the wrong place, can act as a poison. In this instance, the wrong place for cells with antigen A is the blood stream of a person whose plasma contains antibody a, since the latter attacks the red cells with antigen A and causes them to clump together in masses that obstruct the flow of blood. Similarly, antibody b in the plasma causes serious trouble if cells containing antigen B are added in a transfusion.

Each person has in his or her plasma the antibodies for whichever antigen or antigens are lacking in his or her own red cells. In other words, group O people have both antibody a and antibody b in their plasma; group A people have antibody b; group B people have antibody a; and group AB people have neither antibody a or b in their plasma. So long as blood is transfused to people of the same blood type, no difficulties of this kind are encountered. But by crossmatching, the wrong combination can mean quick death for the recipient of the whole blood; foreign cells of the wrong type are quickly clumped into masses resembling clots.

The inheritance of human blood groups shows an additional feature, in that the recessive condition can be concealed by either of two different dominant conditions. One dominant (symbol I^A) causes antigen A to form in the red cells. The other dominant (symbol I^B) causes antigen B to form in the red cells. The recessive (symbol i) does not cause any antigen to form.

People with the genetic constitution $I^A I^A$ or $I^A i$ have only antigen A in the cells and consequently belong to blood group A. People with the genetic constitution $I^B I^B$ or $I^B i$ have only antigen B, and belong to blood group B. People with the genetic constitution $I^A I^B$ have both antigens A and B, hence belong to blood group AB. People with the genetic constitution ii have neither antigen, and belong to blood group O.

From a knowledge of the blood groups to which a mother and her child belong, it is possible to state quite definitely to what blood group the father could belong. Or, where interchange of babies in a hospital is suspected, it is possible to learn from the blood groups of the two parents to what blood groups the child could belong.

The most recent addition to the list of inheritable antigens in man was discovered first in the rhesus monkey, and given the popular name "the Rh factor." Its importance lies in the fact that a break sometimes develops in the placenta through which the unborn child pumps its own blood close to the mother's blood. Through such a break, some of the child's red blood cells may pass into the mother's circulation. If the child's blood is "Rh positive" and the mother's is "Rh negative," the child's cells in the mother's blood stream are almost sure to induce her to form protective antibodies which destroy Rh-positive cells. These antibodies then pass through the break into the child's blood stream, and destroy its red blood cells there, too. This impairs the value of the child's blood as a distributor of oxygen, and may result in irreparable damage to its brain or even in death.

Before the discovery of the Rh factor and its simple mode of inheritance, no one understood why so many babies were still born or delivered with certain incurable difficulties. Now it is easy to test the blood of girls and find those few who are Rh-negative. It is important never to give Rh-negative girls or women Rh-positive blood in a transfusion, for this too can lead to formation of antibodies against Rh-positive cells. Even if the transfusion is made during childhood, the antibodies remain and may cause trouble many years later when she becomes pregnant—if her child is Rh-positive. Only an Rh-negative child is safe in an Rh-negative mother.

Blood cells are Rh-positive when the heredity includes the dominant factor represented by the symbol *Rh*. Rh-positive people have the genetic make-up indicated by either *Rh Rh* or *Rh rh*. If the father is *Rh Rh* and the mother is Rh-negative (*rh rh*), every child will be Rh-positive (*Rh rh*). If the father is *Rh rh*, there will be a 50 per cent chance that each unborn child will be Rh-negative and hence safe.

Rh-negative people are rare among members of the Mongoloid race. About 6 per cent of Negroes show the recessive condition (*rh rh*). Among Caucasoids, however, the proportion varies from about 6 per cent in highland people of the Near East to nearly 30 per cent among the Basque people in the Pyrenees along the border between France and Spain.

Information on human inheritance accumulates slowly. Fortunately, the genetic principles applying to mankind are the same as those that govern guinea pigs, fruit flies, molds, and garden peas. The first "laws of heredity" were discovered, in fact, in edible peas, by the Austrian monk Gregor Johann Mendel in the monastery at Brunn. Mendel had no idea how the heredity was carried from one generation to the next, but he devised the system of symbols that is still used to indicate the genetic make-up of an individual and the constitution of a reproductive cell.

From 1865, when Mendel published an account of his discoveries in the *Proceedings* of the Natural History Society of Brunn, until 1900, no one conducted experiments to learn more of heredity. But between 1900 and 1916 so much was learned about inheritance in animals, particularly in the little fruit fly *Drosophila,* that Dr. Thomas Hunt Morgan of Columbia University was able to offer an extraordinarily useful "theory of the gene." When this theory was found to account for many previously puzzling features of heredity, Dr. Morgan was awarded a Nobel Prize—the first for work in genetics.

According to this theory, each inherited characteristic is determined by something located at a definite site along the length of a specific chromosome. Dr. Morgan named this determiner a "gene." Every chromosome contains many genes, all in a single line. The fruit fly *Drosophila,* which has only four different chromosomes, has about 10,000 genes. These control all of the growth and maturation processes that occur in this particular animal.

When large numbers of crosses have been made to study characteristics controlled by genes in a particular chromosome, it becomes possible to draw a map of the chromosome and show the location of each gene. For the fruit fly *Drosophila* the exact location of several hundred genes has been learned. A smaller number have been located on the twenty-three different chromosomes in the nuclei of human cells.

The chemical nature of the gene became a challenge. Chemists discovered that at the site of each gene in a chromosome was a minute mass of a special protein—a nucleoprotein—found almost exclusively in the cell nuclei. Any nucleoprotein consists of a nucleic-acid portion linked to a purely protein portion. Only the nucleic-acid portion has significance in heredity.

The particular nucleic acid in the nucleoprotein in the gene location in a chromosome is a type called deoxyribonucleic acid (abbreviated DNA), because part of the molecule is the five-carbon sugar known as deoxyribose. The DNA molecule appears to be a spiral ladder, of which the sides consist of alternating units of sugar and phosphate; between the sugar units on opposite sides are rung-like parts which are the key to heredity. They are similar to the letters in a code, serving to "spell out" the directions a gene can give in the living animal.

The nature of these directions is now known. The code in each gene specifies, either directly or indirectly, the pattern the cell must follow in making some particular enzyme. Enzymes must be present in minute amounts if the proper chemical reactions in cells are to occur. Each reaction depends upon a different enzyme. Since enzymes are proteins, they are composed of amino acid molecules linked together. Each gene directs the cell in linking different amino acids in the correct sequence to make the particular protein that will serve as the enzyme for one chemical reaction. Unless the "code" in the rung-like parts of a DNA molecule (a gene) provides the hereditary directions, one enzyme will be missing and its chemical reaction impossible.

The dominant condition of the gene for black hair in guinea pigs leads skin cells to produce an enzyme for a chemical reaction changing a colorless compound into a black pigment. The recessive condition of this gene leads to an absence of both enzyme and pigment—and a white guinea pig.

Many of the characteristics of genes arise from the ladder-like nature of their DNA molecules. Apparently each side of the nucleic-acid ladder contains the full hereditary code. When split lengthwise, it can serve as a reliable guide upon which the cell supplies the missing parts, providing two identical genes where one was before. Whole chromosomes duplicate themselves and all their genes by splitting lengthwise before cell division; each half becomes a chromosome in its own right, with all the inheritable characteristics lined up in exactly the same order. In this way each of the daughter cells after division can be provided with the same hereditary directions as were contained in the nucleus of the parent cell.

Genes show amazing stability as they are reduplicated perhaps millions or billions of times in the cell divisions that accompany embryonic growth of a multicellular animal. They are stable, too, from one generation to the next, while the special type of division parcels out one set of chromosomes to each reproductive cell, and while these cells combine in pairs to provide the basis for a new individual. For thousands of generations, each gene ordinarily continues with no alteration. As a result, the chemistry of life shows this same extraordinary stability.

Over very long periods, genes do change, perhaps spontaneously. The code in the nucleic acid seems to alter one "letter" and spell out a different protein, a different enzyme, a different chemical process for the living cell. Usually these sudden changes (called mutations) are detrimental. Occasionally they are for the good.

Ordinarily, mutations are from the dominant condition of the gene to the recessive, although this does not mean that mutation itself shows any preference in direction. Rather it is due to the fact that each creature's inheritance is composed principally of dominant genes, ones that are advantageous or at least not noticeably harmful. A damaging recessive can be carried hidden in its inheritance—as can also a beneficial recessive. But a damaging dominant is apparent at once. Usually it is weeded out rapidly. Its possessor leaves fewer or no offspring to continue the defective line.

Most of the different "varieties" or "strains" seen in man's domesticated plants and animals began as mutations that appeared spontaneously and were saved—perpetuated by deliberate crossings to get them into combinations for which man could see a value.

Rarely does a mutation confer a benefit advantageous under wild conditions. The strain of domestic pig with extra ribs (hence extra pork chops) is no better able to survive on its own in the forest. The cow that gives twice as much milk as a calf can use is no better mother to a single calf. Nor is the sheep whose wool is twice as heavy any more suited to escaping from wolves on a mountain side. The normal number of ribs, quantity of milk, and thickness of fur are adequate for survival under ordinary circumstances. And although a laboratory strain of white rats is less subject to disease, grows more rapidly, matures earlier, shows greater ability to learn the way through a maze, and becomes senile later than the ancestral type of wild rat in the garbage dump, it cannot compete under garbage-dump conditions.

Mutations tell us much of the operation of inheritance, and appear to be the basis as well for evolution. Consequently, geneticists have spent millions of hours hunting for mutants among their strains of captive animals. For this reason they were delighted when Dr. H. J. Muller, then of the University of Texas, discovered a way to increase the rate at which mutations appear. A moderate dose of X-rays has this effect. His laboratory technique became so important that the Nobel Prize committee awarded Dr. Muller the second such award in genetics as recognition for his discovery.

Radiations from radioactive materials are like X-rays in their effect upon genes. Their influence on evolution is greatest among creatures like insects, which have large families and go through generation after generation at intervals of only a few weeks or months. During the special divisions by which reproductive cells are formed, a new mutation can be combined with an enormous number of other inheritable variations. The larger the family, the more different combinations can appear. Any advantageous ones have a chance to show up, perhaps in time to save a species of animal from becoming extinct when its environment changes. An example from the last twenty years is the modern type of housefly, which differs from its ancestors of only two decades ago in being able to tolerate large doses of DDT and other insecticides.

Each new generation is a testing ground for the variability insured during formation of reproductive cells, through mating of individuals with unlike inheritance, and through novelties introduced by occasional mutations. The fruit fly *Drosophila*, which comes in throngs unbidden to ripe fruit in harvest time, has gone through as many generations since

1900 (when genetics began as a field for scientific investigation) as man has since about 48,000 B.C. Since 1900 they have had as much genetic opportunity to evolve into more successful fruit flies as mankind has had to better itself since the days when Neanderthalers took refuge in caves or hunted the now-extinct mammoths and saber-toothed tigers.

Anything that increases mutation rate, such as artificial radioactivity from nuclear explosions, assists man's competitors among the insects, the bacteria, and the fungi.

In his 1863 address in a Gettysburg cemetery, President Abraham Lincoln set forth a widely held belief: "All men are created equal." He referred to fair equality under the law, not to identity in ability or any other way. No two individuals are exactly alike. Even the "identical twins" who come from separated halves of a single fertilized egg show dissimilarities in fingerprint pattern and other details. (This fact was ignored by the famous British nerve specialist Kinnier Wilson when he described identical twins as "one biological individual masquerading as two people.")

Ordinary "fraternal twins" are scarcely more alike than children born to the same parents in different years. And when careful observations are made on other animals, whether domesticated ones, wild ones, or those such as the cockroach that have adopted man's home and food as theirs, each individual is found to be what the word implies—an individual, identical with no other in body or behavior.

Asexual Reproduction

No difference has been found in the nuclei of the cells in identical twins. Their unlikenesses, though slight, arise from shades of inequality in the division of the cytoplasm between the first two cells in the egg's development. Similar differences presumably could be found between buds produced by a single freshwater hydra, although all the cells of parent and buds arose by ordinary cell division and hence would contain exactly the same genes in precisely identical conditions of dominance and recessiveness. Variation among these offspring is certainly at a minimum.

The same is not true of the drones in a beehive—males produced by parthenogenesis (literally "virgin birth"). The eggs from which they develop are formed by the special type of division that parcels out one complete set of chromosomes into each reproductive cell. This random process guarantees variation among the eggs. Drones merely develop without the additionally varied heritage from a father's sperm cells. All of a drone's cells possess a single set of chromosomes, instead of the usual double set. When a drone forms sperm cells, he does so by ordinary cell division; all sperm from one drone are presumably identical. A queen, however, usually mates with several drones in succession during her nuptial flights. For this reason, her offspring can include new queen bees with a highly variable heritage.

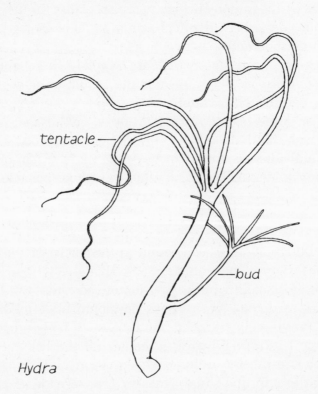

tentacle—

—bud

Hydra

Drone honeybees correspond more closely to the "father-less" frogs that can be produced experimentally from un-fertilized frog eggs, if these are shaken or stimulated chem-ically or pricked gently to start embryonic development on its way. From any batch of eggs suitably treated, a small num-ber will produce tadpoles which seem normal. If they are given suitable living conditions, these fatherless tadpoles will transform into frogs capable of forming eggs—but never sperm cells. This is because the treatment of the eggs causes the two nuclei formed prior to the first cell division to fuse as though they were the nuclei from egg and sperm cells. Since the egg has an X-chromosome to begin with, the father-less frogs are all of the genetic make-up XX, and hence females.

Another example of parthenogenesis has been famous ever since the French entomologist Charles Bonnet dis-covered it in the early 1700's. Plant lice (aphids) hatching from heavy-shelled eggs in the spring of the year are all fe-males. In their ovaries they produce by ordinary cell divi-sion a great many egglike bodies properly called partheno-gonidia. These develop within the mother into young female aphids, which emerge only when they are ready to walk about and feed independently. They grow and soon begin produc-ing parthenogonidia of their own. Each daughter plant louse is the sucking image of her mother. She is a separate indi-vidual, yet except in age, she is an identical twin of the parent who bore her.

On the basis of his discovery, Bonnet proposed a now-overthrown theory of animal reproduction. He believed he could see young aphids ready to grow and unfold, enclosed in the bodies of larger unborn aphids within the obvious parent. He concluded that the series went on endlessly, with all future generations of any animal already preformed within the ones alive today. Or, to apply this idea to human reproduction and the Biblical story of Adam and Eve, Bon-net decided that within Eve's body must have been represen-tatives of all future members of the human race, each enclosed in the next larger like a nesting set of Chinese boxes. What a long way science has come in two centuries, that now we can visualize the reduplication of inherited features in terms of the codes carried by spiral, ladderlike molecules of nucleic acids at definite locations in specific chromosomes, all ready to spell out proteins as enzymes for protoplasmic chemical processes!

Plant lice do not give up sexual reproduction altogether. As autumn approaches, the latest generation of parthenogenetically produced females begins to bear two new types of wingless females. One of these new types produces only young that grow to become winged males. The other type correspondingly yields young that mature into winged females. The winged individuals of both sexes produce sex cells by meiosis, with a full range of variability in the individual nuclei. The eggs are laid after fertilization, covered in a heavy shell that resists desiccation, and with a protoplasm that is almost immune to injury by frost. These are among the eggs that chickadees and nuthatches eat as they explore bark crevices and branch surfaces during the winter. Yet enough eggs of plant lice remain undisturbed in spring to start another season of wingless female aphids on their parthenogenetic way.

The Importance of Sex

That meiotic divisions and fusion of sex cells in pairs precede formation of winter eggs in plant lice is a tribute to the importance of sex among living things. It is important because of the variability introduced among the offspring. Part of this arises through the fresh combinations parcelled out in the nuclei of the sex cells. Part comes through the combination of two unlike parental lines.

The versatile, rather than the meek, inherit the earth. Sex aids that versatility. Here is the answer to the central problem: Why sex? It replies also to the perennial inquiry: Is the male necessary? He contributes his microscopic sperm—

so insignificantly small they remained unknown until less than three centuries ago. But he adds immeasurably to the variation among the offspring and thereby earns himself a real importance. His life may be brief but his effect is enormous.

Sexual reproduction seems to be the best solution to the challenges met in providing a continued lifestream of intricate animals flowing into the future. A male, a female, and their family of unlike offspring. A race full of variation and versatility—adapting itself to the future as the future becomes the present, and evolving slowly like a superorganism. A kingdom of animals advancing, depending on, and cooperating with their distant kin the plants—each kind using sex in special ways toward identical goals. These are the ways in which life becomes a vibrant tide swelling around the ever-changing earth, constantly stirring its inherited past with the force of sex, and battling the present for the right to a posterity.

CHAPTER

7

Animals in the Balance of Nature

The slipper animalcule *Paramecium,* which thrives on bacteria in a hay infusion, is a single-celled animal about $\frac{1}{10}$ of an inch in length and $\frac{1}{50}$ of an inch in each of the other dimensions. Each one weighs about 32 millionth of an ounce. When given enough to eat and space in a few drops of watery hay infusion, each paramecium kept at a comfortable room temperature becomes two individuals, which grow and are themselves ready to divide in from twenty to twenty-two hours.

If all of the offspring from one insignificant paramecium were to survive and reproduce at this rate, starting on January 1 with a mere $\frac{1}{25000}$ of a cubic inch of protoplasm, the total would be a whole cubic inch before January 22 (twenty-four generations), a cubic foot before February 2, a cubic mile by the 72nd generation (March 7), a volume equal to that of the earth by the 112th generation, and a bulk larger than that of the entire universe before Christmas time.

This ability to continue reproduction at the same pace was verified by experiment. At Yale University the late Professor L. L. Woodruff carried a culture of parameciums through 11,000 counted generations. His task required nearly thirty years. In human beings, 11,000 generations would take about 3,000 centuries—from 298,000 B.C. to the present. Professor Woodruff was able to manage his experiment only because he regularly killed the extra individuals as rapidly as they reproduced.

Under wild conditions, every kind of animal reproduces at a rate that could not possibly be supported on the earth if all offspring were to survive. In place of the professor's monitoring hand, the environment—both nonliving and living— eliminates all but a few in each generation. The total number of every kind of animal is reduced to an essentially constant level. Only by close adherence to this schedule is each species kept from becoming extinct or overrunning all of its neighbors.

The elephant reproduces very slowly. From eighteen months to two years elapse between the date of mating and the birth of a baby. The mother bears just one at a time, and may wait another year before mating again. Hence a single offspring at three-year intervals is average. Yet, over the centuries, the world would become trampled by a multitude of elephants if the environment did not limit the survivors to one new adult for every adult that dies. The oceans would become filled with oysters that, year after year, each liberate between a hundred million and five hundred million eggs annually. Or by the Pacific salmon, each pair of which drops the basis for three hundred thousand new lives in a gravelly depression far up some mountain stream.

Competition for food and space is so severe that to insure even one new pair of parents ready to take the place of each pair passing reproductive age requires animals to be fitted remarkably well into their individual ways of life. This fit is achieved through differences in body build, in inner chemistry, and through a flexible interplay of reflexes, instincts, and learned behavior. These differences are regarded as adaptations—modifications away from a sort of average animal of the particular type. The African elephant differs from elephants in general in having particularly large ears. It lives in open savannas on the central plateau where the sun is hot, and gets rid of body heat through the broad surfaces of its ears. The Indian elephant, which lives in shady woodlands, never grows as large as the African elephant. Even with small ears, matching the narrower spaces between the trees, it gets rid of its excess heat through its proportionally larger body surface. The extinct mammoth, which lived close to the glaciers of the Ice Ages, wore a heavy coat of fur. Still other elephants of long ago had four tusks instead of only two, probably in relation to their particular way of life.

Adaptations Related to Food

The elephant's trunk is a grasping organ of tremendous power, with which the animal can break the tops from medium-sized trees and bring edible foliage within reach. The elephant uses its tusks as tools in digging, as well as weapons in defense. Yet the tusks are merely enlarged canine teeth, and the trunk a greatly extended nose.

An almost endless list could be compiled, drawing attention to the ways in which body features show specializations in relation to definite uses. Differences in the teeth related to the types of food were mentioned in the chapter on Land Animals. Aquatic vertebrates show comparable adaptations. The teeth of sharks are sharp, set in multiple rows, and replaced as they become worn from seizing and tearing flesh. Skates and rays, which are closely related to sharks, have teeth with flattened tops, suitable for crushing shellfish to get the meat inside. Bony fishes usually possess small teeth that prevent prey from escaping during the slow process of swallowing.

The mouthparts of insects show what a great range of possibilities are available in one basic set of appendages. All of them are modifications of an upper lip, a pair of jaws working from side to side, a pair of food-manipulating organs (the maxillae), and a lower lip.

In grasshoppers the jaws are particularly sturdy, and find use in biting out pieces of foliage, usually along the edge of a leaf. Scimitar-shaped jaws with sharp points enable a tiger beetle to seize its prey. Ant lions, which are the young of insects somewhat resembling a dragonfly, possess scimitar-shaped jaws, too, but each jaw is hollow and contains a duct from the salivary glands, extending as a tube to the needle-sharp jaw tip. The ant lion seizes an ant or other insect victim in these jaws, injects a generous amount of saliva, and then waits until the toxic digestive agents in the secretion paralyze the victim and liquefy its internal organs. When digestion is fairly complete, the ant lion uses the same hollow jaws as soda straws through which to suck in the liquid body contents of the prey, leaving only an empty shell.

The caterpillar stage of butterflies and moths has jaws similar to those of a grasshopper, and attends to the task of feeding and storing food so efficiently that the adult can afford to sip only nectar and dew. The spiral nectar straw that a butterfly or moth uncurls from under its head is actually the two food-handling appendages (maxillae) fitted together to leave a water-tight passage way between them; the jaws and other mouth parts are small.

The sucking mouths of true bugs, such as plant lice (aphids) and the bedbug, and of various flies, such as mosquitoes, consist of a tube-shaped extension of the lower lip, surrounding needle-sharp piercing stylets representing the paired jaws and the paired food-handling maxillae. The same type of lower lip is of very different shape in the grotesque immature stages of dragonflies and damselflies; it forms a sort of mask held over the front of the head except during the moment when the insect thrusts it far in advance of the body as a grasping organ able to seize prey and drag it back to the mouth. The fleshy lobe with which a housefly stamps over the surface of a sugar lump, on the other hand, is its specialized upper lip, and the rest of its mouthparts are very small.

Adaptations sometimes permit animals to use as food an

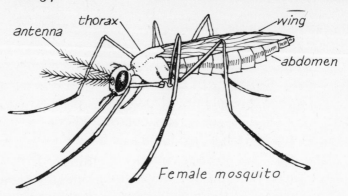

Female mosquito

unselected assortment of particles each of which is far too small to be detected separately. Oysters, clams, barnacles, and many burrowing worms depend upon minute bits of life they can strain from the water. This is "filter-feeding," a technique used also by the myriad small swimming crustaceans and immature fish of many kinds in the sea and fresh waters.

The giant whalebone whales are filter-feeders, and on this insignificant-appearing food reach the greatest bulk of any animal known. Whalebone, which is a horny material formed during embryonic growth through the fusion of long hairs rimming the whale's mouth, hangs in long narrow flexible plates from the edge of the upper jaw. It serves as an efficient strainer upon which the whale can close its mouth at intervals. The animal distends its great tongue with blood and squeezes the trapped victims from between the whalebone plates into its throat.

After food has been captured or engulfed, adaptations may enable the animal to store particles before digestion begins. Chipmunks and hamsters often scamper around like animated vacuum cleaners, filling special cheek pouches at each side of the mouth with food to be carried to underground storehouses. The gullet of birds, earthworms, and leeches is distended into a crop, where large meals can be stored until digestion takes care of the accumulation. In birds and earthworms, the crop is followed by a specialized part of the stomach—the gizzard, which can be armed with abrasive materials such as small stones used in shredding the food. Gizzard stones were important to the dinosaurs of long ago, and are still used by crocodilians today.

Often the sense organs of an animal show special sensitivity in relation to food. Smell aids the dog in finding a buried bone, whereas vision alone seems vital to a soaring hawk or a darting flycatcher. A hawk or an eagle has the equivalent of a telescope built into each eye. The light-sensitive cells and nerve connections to the brain are several times finer than those in a human eye, and permit the bird to see great detail at a distance. A soaring bird of prey can detect a grasshopper or a mouse from a height at which each of these would be invisible to the unaided human eye.

Sensitivity to radiant heat appears to be developed highly in mosquitoes and other blood-sucking insects. For this reason they alight more readily upon dark clothing and dark skins than upon white clothing and white skins. A comparable adaptation is found among the pit-vipers, such as rattlesnakes and water moccasins. The "pit" is a large, shallow, conical depression on each side of the head, between nostril and eye. These pits are sensitive to radiant heat, and allow the snake to hunt in the dark. With their aid, a pit-viper can aim with remarkable accuracy in complete darkness, and strike the body of a bird or mammal, or a wet-skinned frog or an ice cube. The snake distinguishes objects that are either conspicuously warmer or cooler than their surroundings, and usually gains a dinner in this way.

Adaptations Related to Finding and Winning Mates

Invertebrate animals include quite a number of kinds that follow the method used by sea stars and oysters, discharging into the water around them millions of eggs and sperm cells, and leaving to chance the meeting of these in fertilization. Most animals are far less casual in reproduction, and through their behavior make more certain that a female's eggs will be fertilized at the correct stage of ripeness. Usually this means that the animal can get along with fewer eggs. On the other hand, it may need to stop feeding and perhaps expose itself to danger while seeking a mate.

Earthworms often encounter neighbors while they are extended from burrow openings in search of food. Apparently each worm depends upon the sense of touch to find a suitable mate, since mated pairs are almost invariably of closely matched size. This allows the longitudinal grooves on the outside of the body of one worm to match those on the other, forming special channels through which the sperm cells can travel between the two. Each earthworm is both male and female and, when mating, donates sperm as well as collects sperm on an exchange basis.

Odor can be a powerful clue serving to bring potential mates together. Male moths fly for a mile or more upwind to a waiting female of their kind. And the time when a pet female cat or dog becomes sexually receptive is usually obvious from the number of tomcats arriving outside to serenade at night, or the sudden interest in the whole household shown by every male dog in the neighborhood.

Many kinds of animals are adapted in ways that let them make sounds and hear these as a form of communication important in finding mates. The tremendous variety of bird songs serves this role, and so do the calls made by various insects such as crickets, katydids, grasshoppers, and cicadas. Fish make sounds and detect them, too. The same is true of frogs and toads, some reptiles, and perhaps most mammals. Hunters often lure target birds and mammals within reach by imitating the mating calls of crows, ducks, moose, and elk.

Most insects and many spiders rely upon visual cues in identifying mates. Birds depend even more upon eyes in finding members of the opposite sex, and in many instances demonstrate an unlearned awareness of color and details of pattern.

In the dark, eyes can be important, too. Luminescent spots and streaks are recognition signals for fishes and squids and a multitude of crustaceans in the black abysses of the sea to which no daylight penetrates, and for fireflies at night over land. The large-eyed male fireflies wing along slowly, flashing their abdominal lamps at irregular intervals. Females perched on foliage flash in response. If the interval between the flash and the response is correct within a few tenths of a second, the male is likely to turn in his flight and alight beside the responsive female.

In many kinds of animals, the males are ready to mate with any cooperative female. This leads to competitions, after which the victor or the survivor becomes the father of the offspring. Often the distinctive features shown by the males have a role in these competitions. Elk and deer use their antlers in combat, one male with another, butting and slashing. The peacock spreads his fan of tail feathers, producing an illusion of impressive size. The hercules beetle *Dynastes* of Haiti uses his tremendous thoracic horn and head horn for dueling and for carrying off a passive female.

Male crickets, katydids, and many kinds of birds use their mating calls as a means of staking out a territory they are ready to defend—a region in which they claim any female as their own. The small American warbler known as the yellowthroat and the British robin redbreast both have this habit. Male yellowthroats wear a conspicuous black mask-like mark across the eyes, whereas the female lacks it. In breeding season, a male yellowthroat will court and attempt to mate with a stuffed skin of a female yellowthroat fastened to a bush. But if an experimenter draws on the stuffed specimen a black mask-shaped mark like that of the male, the live male makes no courtship gestures. Instead, he dashes at the effigy, tearing it to pieces with beak and claws. The male British robin will court a mounted skin of his own sex if the red feathers of the breast have been painted a dull brown like those of the female, but he will attack even a tuft of feathers in his territory if they have the color of his own red breast. At mating time, many male birds will tire themselves trying to drive away their own reflection in a window pane.

Adaptations That Provide for the Young

Eggs and young are so defenseless that any assistance given them by the parents tends to reduce mortality among them, and permit more of them to reach reproductive maturity. Adaptations providing assistance in this way are often as simple as for the parent to hide her eggs.

A number of habits shown by one or both parents, helpful to the young, were mentioned in the chapter on reproduction. These behaviors are among the most fascinating in the whole range of the animal kingdom.

Birds are particularly famous for the care they give their nestlings—shading them from sun, brooding over them when the temperature falls, bringing them food which may be whole (as in wrens and other insect-eating birds), or partly digested (as in most fish- and seed-eaters), or a special secretion from glands in the crop (as in the pigeons). The mother may attend to these tasks unaided by a mate, as is usual in hummingbirds. Or the two parents may cooperate, as is usual among water birds. Little grebes, geese (goslings), and swans (cygnets) frequently snuggle into the back feathers of one parent while the other goes for food. The one adult then cruises over the lake or river as a warm, dry ferryboat and the mate brings food to the young, making trip after trip for this purpose alone.

Some of the social insects are equally remarkable. Several kinds of ants and many types of termites maintain fungus gardens in their nests. An edible fungus, which thrives on vegetation brought in and manured by the insects, supplies a food important to both adults and young.

Adaptations Valuable in Defense or Escape

Perhaps the best of all ways to survive to reproductive maturity is to live without being seen, in a region where food is plentiful. The larger herbivorous animals, such as antelope and deer, are conspicuous if they feed on an open plain by day. Even at night they can be recognized and pounced on by keen-eyed predators, such as lions and wolves. Most of these herbivores are long-legged and fleet; their ability to run rapidly is matched by acute hearing and sense of smell. And when not feeding, each ordinarily seeks out the shelter of vegetation, where body coloration and markings so often provide protection in the ways man has come to describe as camouflage. Partly this is a matter of matching the brightness or darkness of the surroundings, and eliminating contrast. Partly the concealment is achieved through marks that are meaningless but distract the eye from the whole outline, and hence reduce the chance of recognition. Sometimes the pattern suggests that of vegetation where the animal hides. Vertical grass blades match the stripes of tigers, zebras, badgers, and bitterns. Or it may suggest spotty shade, as do the pale spots on the young of tapirs and on the fawns of deer. Some insects resemble leaves or bird droppings or bark or twigs or thorns. So long as they remain still when in danger, they are well protected.

Only a few animals adjust their color or pattern in ways that improve the match with the background upon which they rest. Changes of this kind have been attributed incorrectly to the true chameleons of Africa and the false chameleons of the southeastern United States. These lizards, like tree frogs, do shift their color through alterations in pigment cells within the skin; but their changes match temperature or excitement rather than background. Flounders and a few kinds of crustaceans, however, do show an astonishing ability to match the bottom or the seaweed among which they settle.

A minority of animals are adapted in ways that permit them to defend themselves. Some have armor in the form of scales, bony plates, or various types of shells. Others possess weapons such as antlers, horns, prominent teeth, or stings. The quills of porcupines are certainly among the most remarkable of these defensive weapons, since each is a modified hair, stiff, hollow, barbed, and easily pulled loose

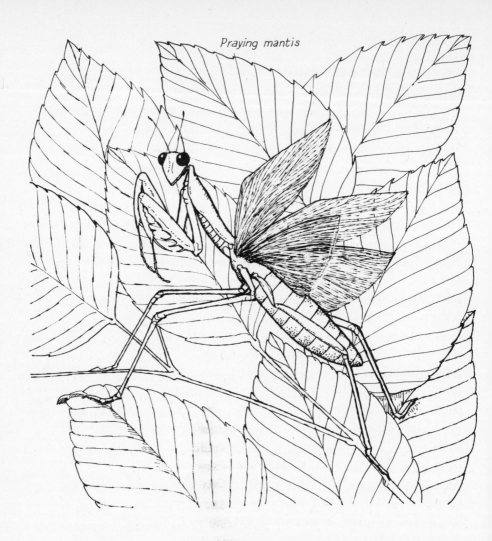

if it becomes embedded in an attacker. The skunk has its rectal glands, opening through a nozzle that the animal can aim at an enemy. The blister beetle secretes a substance at its knee joints that has a violent action on human skin.

A more drastic method of defense is found in animals such as crabs, crayfish and lobster, sea stars and sea cucumbers, and various long-tailed lizards. These creatures are ready at a moment's notice to break free from parts of their bodies, and to follow this self-mutilation within a reasonable time by regeneration of the lost part. The tail shed by a frightened lizard may snap into still smaller portions, and each piece twitch vigorously for a few minutes, serving often to distract a predator while the lizard escapes.

Several kinds of harmless flies that frequent the same flowers as stinging bees and wasps are almost indistinguishable in color and outline and behavior when seen with the armed insects. A practiced eye is needed to distinguish the unarmed "mimic" from the armed "model." Perhaps the commonest of the deceivers is the drone fly *Eristalis tenax*, found on both sides of the North Atlantic Ocean. It may well have been the basis for Samson's story of the honeybees in a dead lion, for the immature stages of the bee-imitating drone fly are the "rat-tailed maggots" found in wet carrion and in exposed sewage.

Social Adaptations

Small, unarmed animals sometimes associate with larger, weapon-bearing kinds without showing any similarity in appearance. If the smaller "guest" benefits without conferring any gain on the larger "host," the association of these animals is called commensalism. Many oysters and mussels conceal a small, round-bodied commensal crab. This is the pea crab, which runs into the mollusk's shell cavity through the water-admitting siphon. The crustacean is free to escape by the same route, or it may remain within the clam's shell, feeding on the larger particles that enter in the feeding-breathing current.

Where Portuguese man-of-wars drift over the warmer oceans of the world, their long blue tentacles dangle or trail below the pink-and-violet iridescent floats. Despite the nettling cells that stud the tentacles, many small commensal fish accompany the man-of-wars, hiding from larger fishes that would pursue and eat them beyond the shelter of the colonial coelenterate. Occasionally one of the small commensal fish does get caught and eaten by the man-of-war, proving that this haven has real dangers as well as advantages.

Sharks, too, have their followers. Many sharks swim along with smaller, slender remoras (shark suckers) clinging to them through the suction-cup action of a specialized back fin. The remora gets free transportation without inconveniencing the shark. When the large predator catches a meal or passes through a school of sardines, the remora frees itself long enough to get something to eat, and then returns to its carrier. Shark suckers seem equally willing to ride below a sea turtle. In the tropics, fishermen sometimes make use of this habit, employing a remora to whose tail a cord has been tied. When the fisherman in a small boat sees a sea turtle swimming a short distance away, he releases the shark sucker and pays out the cord attached to it. When the remora gets a good grip below the turtle's shell, the man in the boat can reel in his cord and his turtle dinner, and recover his shark sucker too.

Social adaptations in some other animals confer two-way benefits. Termites of many kinds depend, in fact, upon a partnership with single-celled protozoans of a type that swims by means of many flagella. The insect in this partnership uses its jaws to get wood fibers broken into fragments small enough to swallow; it is unable, however, to digest the cellulose cell walls of the wood. The protozoan partners live in the alimentary canal of the termite, where they have no way to obtain wood fibers through their own efforts. But they can and do digest cellulose, breaking the big carbohydrate molecule down into sugars. After the protozoans have done their work, the termite is able to absorb nourishment derived from the wood it chewed and swallowed. The whole organization of the termite colony and many of the habits of its inmates are usually linked to the essential task of sharing live protozoans—passing them from insect to insect, and insuring a means for getting nourishment out of the food eaten.

Other partnerships exemplifying "mutualism" often include participants, one of which is an animal and the other a plant. The cud-chewing herbivores depend upon cellulose-splitting bacteria. The human digestive tract absorbs far more nourishment for us from the food we eat because of the presence in it of certain bacteria that break down large molecules or synthesize vitamins. Vitamin K, needed if the blood is to clot properly, is an example. Until a human baby acquires its intestinal partners, it may need injections of vitamin K to insure correct functioning of its blood stream.

One of the strangest examples of mutualism allows the giant of all clams, the bear's paw *Tridacna,* to attain a shell weight of more than 500 pounds in the coral reefs of the South Pacific. Paradoxically, it accomplishes this growth while eating less than other clams. The bear's paw lies embedded in the reef with its hinge downward. When sea water covers it by day, it spreads the wavy edges of its heavy shell and pushes out a thick purple mantle dotted with minute glistening flecks. For a time these spots were believed to be eyes. Instead, they are windows admitting light into chambers in the fleshy mantle where the clam raises microscopic algae as food. With carbon dioxide from the clam's respiration and water from its blood, the algae use the light in photosynthesis, as the basis for growth and reproduction. The clam's white blood cells then harvest the algae.

When an animal of small size takes its nourishment at the expense of a large animal, the little one is referred to as a parasite. Those parasites that stay on the outside of the host's body (as "ectoparasites") seldom cause any direct damage unless they become exceedingly numerous. However, they may transfer disease, or cause itching so intense that the host is distracted from important activities, such as eating or reproducing.

Fleas, whose flattened bodies let them slip easily between the bases of hairs or feathers when the host becomes irritated into scratching, are parasites only as adults, when their mouthparts are lancetlike, fitting them from breaking into the host's blood stream. Their hind legs are specialized, too, enabling them to perform prodigious leaps to reach a host or jump from one to another. Lice, on the other hand, are parasitic as soon as they hatch from the egg. They travel by crawling and feed in most instances entirely on dead skin. Their adaptations include highly specialized legs with which they can cling tightly to skin or hairs.

Internal parasites ("endoparasites") include a large number of different kinds that live in and obtain their nourishment from the blood of the host. Many of them are like the protozoans causing malaria and African sleeping sickness in depending upon some blood-sucking insect to act as a transferring agent (vector), carrying them from host to host.

The vector insect for malaria is the *Anopheles* mosquito, which sucks up many waiting individuals of the parasite whenever it takes a blood meal from a malaria sufferer. The parasites mate and reproduce within the mosquito, and then migrate to the salivary glands, requiring almost two weeks to reach that part of the insect. A mosquito with malaria parasites in its salivary glands injects the protozoans along with saliva whenever it bites. In the blood of the new host that has been bitten by the infected mosquito, the malaria protozoans travel and reproduce in tissues as widely separated as the liver and the marrow of the long bones such as femur and tibia. Then they begin invading red blood cells.

Within a red blood cell, a single malaria parasite becomes a dozen or more, destroying the hemoglobin as food in the process. This new generation bursts into the plasma, each individual ready to attack a fresh red cell. Commonly the generations of malaria parasites emerge almost simultaneously from millions of red blood cells, and liberate into the blood poisons to which the host reacts with chills and fever. As the parasites invade new red cells, the poison is dissipated and the host recovers—only to be struck down again by a new round of chills and fever in a few days when the next reproductive cycle of the parasite is completed.

African sleeping sickness is caused by parasitic protozoans called trypanosomes. Although the parasites can swim by means of whiplashlike flagella, they are carried from one victim to the next by a blood-sucking fly—the tsetse fly *Glossina*. Over a large part of Africa where tsetse flies live, the trypanosomes are common in the blood of wild animals such as elephants, buffaloes, antelopes, owls, crocodiles, and even snakes. Most of these host animals show no symptoms of illness due to the trypanosomes. Yet they serve as a great reservoir from which the flies transfer infection to native people, to incoming settlers, and to domesticated livestock. In all of these the infection commonly is fatal as soon as the parasites attack the nervous system and block any interest in physical activity—even eating. The sick animal or person wants only to sleep, and from this the disease takes its common name.

Parasites inside the intestinal tract are even commoner than those in the blood stream. Since they must reach a position in the alimentary canal in order to get food, the adaptations of intestinal parasites are concerned chiefly with insuring that the host will get them into its stomach. For the most part, intestinal parasites not only have to eat, but have to be eaten. Their life cycles may be simple or highly complex, but all tend to insure that the parasite will reach its internal goal.

The ameba causing amebic dysentery has one of the simplest life histories of any internal parasite. The animal itself is a single cell about 1/1000th inch in diameter, a protozoan that gains entry to the digestive tract by way of contaminated drinking water. The ameba attacks living cells of the intestinal wall, and releases waste materials that cause severe diarrhea. Its full name *Endamoeba histolytica* ("the internal ameba that destroys tissues") describes its activities well. Amebas in drinking water can be killed by boiling. Treating amebas that have become established in the alimentary canal is much more difficult; the victim must then swallow drugs that will destroy the parasites without endangering human life. Without treatment, the victim is likely to decline in general health to a point where some other, more fatal disease invades and causes the death of the host.

In the tropics where amebic dysentery is common, it is regarded as an important factor shortening human life.

Many of the intestinal worms work in the same vague way. They do not kill their hosts, but they lower resistance to other diseases.

Tapeworms are of many kinds, some of the common ones requiring two different hosts. They mature in the digestive tract of a vertebrate animal, each tapeworm attached by means of a specialized individual called the scolex. This individual bears muscular suckers or anchoring hooks with which to hold to the wall of the small intestine while it absorbs digested food from its surroundings. The scolex grows rapidly at its free end, forming there a series of new individuals called proglottids. The proglottids do not separate for some time, but soon they extend away from the scolex in a succession of units forming a ribbonlike colony—the tapeworm.

While the whole worm keeps itself looped back and forth in the fluid contents of the host's intestine by gentle swimming movements, its proglottids mature and engage in sexual reproduction. Each proglottid matures first as a male with testes. Later, these sex organs degenerate and are replaced by ovaries—making the proglottid a female. These older, female proglottids receive sperm cells from younger proglottids, and their eggs begin to develop immediately. By the time the embryos in the eggs have approached the hatching stage, the proglottid containing them is near the end of the colonial chain and ready to break free, to be cast out with fecal wastes.

Except for the ripe proglottids full of embryos discharged in the feces, there may be no sign of the parasite's presence in the host animal. The demands of the tapeworm are small. One tapeworm in the intestine of a person who eats well is probably of little consequence. In fact, the largest and healthiest looking of house cats frequently contain several of their own kinds of tapeworm or one of the types that can infect man. Yet month after month, year after year, the tapeworm continues to grow and release proglottids full of embryos that are ready to burst from the egg shells.

In primitive societies where pigs are raised as food, the pigs usually have opportunity to eat the infected human feces. As soon as the tapeworm proglottid reaches the pig's intestine, the embryo worms hatch and continue their development within the pig as the second host. Soon they reach a stage in which they invade the intestinal blood vessels and ride along in the blood to the pig's muscles. There each larval tapeworm embeds itself and secretes a surrounding wall within which it transforms. It becomes a "bladder worm"—a name referring to the bladderlike bag in which it rests.

Primitive societies have no meat inspector to guard the public by condemning pork with bladder worms. And if the pork is cooked inadequately before it is eaten by man, the bladder worms reach the human digestive tract unharmed. There they unfold. Each becomes the scolex of a new tapeworm. Within a year, a pork tapeworm in a well-fed person may measure 25 feet from the scolex to the ripest proglottid, yet still fit nicely inside the eight or ten feet of small intestine.

Sanitary disposal of human feces, careful inspection of meat, thorough cooking of pork, and even the cooking of all garbage that is to be fed to pigs, are methods that break the life cycle of the pork tapeworm. Similar steps are needed to prevent the spread of other kinds of tapeworms whose resting stages await man in beef, fish, and meat products.

Undercooked pork is dangerous to man because of another common parasite, the roundworm *Trichinella* (often called the trichina worm). Properly this worm is adapted to a life cycle with the pig as one host and the rat as the other. Pigs eat dead rats whenever possible, or slaughterhouse scraps and garbage containing meat infected with *Trichinella*. The larval worms are freed by the pig's own digestive action. They mature rapidly in the contents of the pig's small intestine and mate there. Female worms then burrow into the intestinal wall and produce young in enormous numbers. Each immature worm penetrates the host's blood vessels and rides the blood stream to the muscles, particularly those of the diaphragm. There each grows to a length of about $\frac{1}{25}$ of an inch at the expense of a single muscle cell, in which it coils up and goes into a dormant state. Beyond this point the worm does not proceed unless it is eaten by another susceptible mammal, although it may await this event for many months.

Rats, cats, dogs, and black bears—all of them scavengers with a liking for meat—can enter the life cycle of *Trichinella*. Man becomes infected by eating inadequately cooked pork or rare bear steak. In terms of the parasite's success, however, human infections in a modern society are usually a complete loss because ordinary methods of embalming and burial either kill the dormant worms or block transfer to another host. Yet a good many people become infected every year in the United States. Heavy infections cause serious symptoms, even death; the disease is called trichinosis.

Metamorphosis

The transformation of parasites, permitting them to match the living habits of several hosts, seem to be remarkable adaptations. They are far from unique. Amphibians and many arthropods regularly go through quite as spectacular changes as each matures.

The tadpole of a frog or toad swims with a muscular tail, uses gills in respiration, and digests its plant foods in a long spiral intestine which often can be seen through the semi-transparent underside of the body. At metamorphosis, the tadpole develops legs, absorbs its tail, abbreviates its alimentary canal, transfers from vegetarian fare to insects, from gills to lungs, from swimming to walking or leaping, from water to air, and quickly becomes expert at flipping out its specialized sticky tongue to capture elusive insects detected through newly enlarged eyes. As an adult it bears a different and distinctive body pattern, makes characteristic calls, and is ready at mating season to make extensive migrations in reaching water where eggs can be laid. In each half of its two-part life cycle the amphibian is excellently adapted to its habits, and well deserves its name (from the Greek *bios*, life, and *amphi-*, of two kinds).

The maggot that becomes a fly or the caterpillar that transforms into a butterfly is equally well adapted to two unlike lives. The caterpillar hatches from the egg, spends its days and sometimes nights as well in devouring foliage, in growing one molt after another, and in storing away fat at the same time that its body increases in bulk. During the late stages of caterpillarhood, special growth centers appear inside its body, and these begin producing the organs of the adult. Finally the caterpillar hunts out a secluded spot and transforms into a nonfeeding stage, the pupa or chrysalis. Within its hard external coating, secreted by the larval skin, the insect lives upon its fat while breaking down all larval organs and building the adult ones to essentially final form. Then it splits its pupal shell and climbs out. Muscular contraction of its abdomen pumps blood into the thin spaces between the membranes of the wings, and these organs expand rapidly to full size, hardening as vanes that can carry the insect aloft when untried muscles contract instinctively in proper sequence.

The adult insect (butterfly) is fitted for flights as brief

as to the next flower for nectar, or as long as from Canada to the Florida Keys and back. This adult has excellent vision, and its nervous system provides for a vast array of instinctive reactions needed in sipping nectar, avoiding enemies, dexterous flight, navigation in migration, mating, and, in the female, identification of the proper plant upon which to deposit the eggs. Since none of these activities correspond to those of the caterpillar stage, it is evident that the animal's body and chemical processes have been reorganized from end to end.

Food Webs

To understand how any animal fares, a person needs to know more than what it does between the moments of fertilization and death—its beginning and end as an individual. Each creature maintains a place for itself in a web of life, and its success or failure is tied up with the fates of a host of other kinds of animals.

A fire in late summer that burns the lichen carpet from a large area of arctic tundra is almost certain to mean starvation for millions of mouselike lemmings; their disappearance will starve the snowy owls, starting hundreds of these birds winging southward far beyond their normal range in search of substitute food; the absence of lichens from the area can force a herd of migrant caribou to change its route and ruin the hunting upon which Eskimo families depend hundreds of miles away along the coast of the Arctic Ocean.

A disease of varying hares (often called "snowshoe rabbits"), carried from one to another by parasitic ticks, may suddenly kill off most members of a large population. On the surviving hares, the ticks have fewer opportunities to find others of their kind and breed—leading to a sudden plunge in the size of the tick population. More noticeably, lynxes and foxes and coyotes and wolves and eagles that ordinarily feed extensively on hares, turn their attention to mice and squirrels, grouse and pheasants, deer and domesticated animals. They may still need to look for other food—even leaves and roots. The increased toll of mice and seed-eating birds allows far larger crops of weed seeds to germinate. The appearance of the whole countryside may change because of the interactions following an alteration in the abundance of some one animal or plant.

Occasionally a food web is restricted in some way, allowing it to be examined closely. In a cave frequented by insect-eating bats, for example, the food available to other animals may be almost entirely dependent upon the undigested residues in bat droppings reaching the cave floor. Night after night the bats emerge, catch insects, and return for the day. Day after day the guano accumulates. Some of it supports a felt of mold. Cave crickets eat the mold, feeding almost continuously; they grow and reproduce rapidly. Cave spiders, cave scorpions, cave centipedes, and cave salamanders all catch crickets, grow, and reproduce. Blood-sucking parasites akin to bedbugs attack the sleepy bats, then leave their hosts and cling to the cave walls. The spiders and scorpions and centipedes and salamanders catch bat bugs, too. Crickets vary their diet of mold by eating young spiders and all the bat bugs they can find.

When winter comes, the bats are likely to migrate toward the Equator where insects are still flying in the night air. The cave temperature remains almost constant, but the source of food for cave animals has disappeared. No fresh droppings fall. The mold cannot grow on the guano as fast as the crickets eat it. Crickets begin to starve. The bat bugs can find no blood meals. As they weaken with starvation, they become prey to hungry crickets, spiders, scorpions, centipedes, and salamanders. Rapidly the whole animal population of the cave shrinks to a few survivors. With luck they feed upon one another and on the feeble mold until the bats return in spring and the plant material begins again to grow luxuriantly.

Charles Darwin drew attention to food relationships among animals, and to the unsteady balance they maintain in each area. He could not help being impressed by the profligate reproduction of every species on the one hand, and by the drastic destruction on the other—preventing any species from overwhelming the rest. In each region the entire community of animals depends for its continuation upon what man regards as extreme waste. Why should a pair of herrings produce 50,000 eggs if only two, on the average, can ever reach reproductive maturity?

The answer is that the missing 49,998 eggs, on the average, are needed either as eggs other animals will eat to keep alive, or as young fish on which sea crustaceans and larger fish depend, or as older fish a shark or sea bird or man will catch. Young herrings that never reach maturity serve as links in the web, as ways in which microscopic green plants in the sea are transformed into animal flesh nourishing the whole community of oceanic life. Even the bacteria on the sea floor, which constantly reproduce while decomposing the organic debris that sinks to the bottom, provide food for sea urchins and sea cucumbers creeping over the ooze and for animals that burrow among the sediments. Rarely is anything organic actually wasted, even though the survivors of each kind are few.

The weight of any creature is related to the weight of the protoplasm in the food it eats. On the average, each pound of body weight represents close to ten pounds of food eaten annually. On this basis, each ton of living whale represents about ten tons of small crustaceans and fishes filtered from the sea each year.

To continue feeding on the same type of food, an animal must not take more than about a third of the available supply in any one year; the remaining two-thirds are needed as a breeding stock, to reproduce itself and maintain the supply. Hence each ton of whale should represent ten tons of living food eaten and twenty additional tons of small crustaceans and fishes left swimming around—a total of thirty tons of food in the sea to match each ton of whale. And these figures refer only to food of importance to the whale.

In the simplest situation, the small crustaceans and fishes used by the whale could be of kinds that depend upon microscopic green algae. This is the only life in the open ocean able to grow and reproduce without dependence upon any other creature. If the same relationships apply, the thirty tons of food animals per ton of whale should correspond to thirty times thirty tons of microscopic green algae—900 tons all told, with 300 tons eaten by the small crustaceans and fishes, and 600 tons of these plants left to continue the supply.

The whale forms the top of a food pyramid, sustained by a mass of thirty times its own weight in small animals which, in turn, are supported by the presence of 900 times their total weight in green plants able to make food with the energy in sunlight. When all of the carnivorous animals in the sea are lumped together, the bulk of vegetarian animals required to feed them and maintain a supply becomes fantastically large. Yet thirty times this total is the measure of the green plants upon which the multitude of food pyramids depends.

On land, a corresponding pyramid can be constructed with grass or trees as the great green base, with rabbits and mice and deer and insects and porcupines as representative herbivorous animals, and with the peak of the living edifice occupied by carnivores such as fox and wolf, eagle and owl. The number of carnivores is always small by comparison with the population of herbivores upon which they feed. The number of herbivores is small in relation to the number of plants. The food pyramid is a pyramid of numbers, too.

For each kind of animal, some few parts of the customary life cycle are the least well adapted to the environment. These are the points at which mortality is highest. Yet no general rule fits them all. In a tropical rain forest, the vulnerable occasion may come when the animal must move about in search of a mate, or stay motionless protecting its young. In an arctic area the critical time is usually winter. Can the creature tolerate the cold and survive until the weather warms enough to permit new sorties in search of food and mates? In a desert the limiting factor is water. Will the animal's hoarded store, plus what it can gain by eating plants and other animals, last until a rainstorm makes the dry land green again?

In the tropics, where a person might expect to find the richness of a zoological exhibit set in a botanical garden, the animals meet intense competition and succeed only by extreme adaptations, particularly those that help them remain invisible for most of their lives. Consequently, a jungle seems uncanny in its emptiness. Close observation is needed to see columns of ants running along the ground, carrying food with them as they go. On branches well above the soil, ant birds wait patiently, motionless, ready to dart after any insect stirred into flight by the marching ants.

Beyond the column of ants on the jungle floor, a fallen branch is growing lighter daily because termites are at work within it. Springtail insects and sow bugs chew beside millipedes on the fallen leaf. But they must work fast to get their share before the molds and bacteria, favored by the warmth and high humidity, cause the plant tissue to vanish through decay.

In the jungle trees, the caterpillar that munches green foliage needs to move as little as possible, and perhaps resemble a bird dropping or a thorn. Many insects eat only at night, when they are less likely to fall prey to a watchful leaflike mantis insect poised in a prayerful attitude, or to a leaf-green tree snake, or to one of the sharp-eyed birds.

Arctic animals that survive the winter include far fewer kinds. Small insects, particularly flies and bees, emerge after a long cold season in the dormant pupal state. Lemmings and caribou that hunt lichens and other plants under the snow are still there. The arctic hare (also called the varying hare and snowshoe rabbit) and the grouselike ptarmigan crouch motionless, while their coats change from pure white to earth-brown in patches that match the melting drifts; they too dig through the snow to reach plant food all winter. The foxes and wolves that catch enough lemmings, hares, and ptarmigans to keep alive through the long cold nights are still ready for more meals of meat. Polar bears and walruses along the coast rely at any season mostly upon food they can reach in the icy water.

Rapidly the days increase in length; the air grows warm; plant life spreads its leaves in the brief spring of the Arctic. Migratory birds arrive from their wintering areas and begin nesting at once, sometimes digging a site in a drift of recent snow. Fur seals crawl out by the millions, bear young, and mate again. Suddenly the carnivorous animals have more to eat than they are able to use. They lie down or stand around, waiting for digestion to make space for another meal. Adaptations that would be meaningful in catching food or in escape from predators decline in importance.

During the short summer of the Far North, bees and nectar-sipping flies have countless blossoms to visit. Bloodsucking flies go through one generation after another, rapidly becoming pestilential. Insectivorous birds can stuff their nestlings with flies almost twenty-four hours a day. Waterfowl find plenty of fresh vegetation to eat. Growth is amazingly fast. All of the adaptations in both animals and plants seem related to shortness of life cycle, such as getting the young birds fledged and flying before the days shorten again and winter weather threatens. Caution has little place in the Arctic, and human visitors are astonished at the raucous sounds, the lack of privacy for nests and dens, and the general unconcern of animals on all sides.

It is no accident that migrant birds of winter residence, whether chickadees and kinglets in the North or penguins in the Southern Hemisphere, tend to be trusting—almost tame. Or that the occasional bird of the tropics, carried far beyond its normal range by storm winds into temperate latitudes, is elusive in the extreme. These differences in behavior match features of importance for survival in their nesting territories. Adaptations must fit the individual to the food web in its home area. Failure to fit almost perfectly is a prelude to early extinction.

C H A P T E R
8

Animals of the Past

Today's animals differ from those of the past in many ways, for every living thing has changed with time and is still changing. Yet all animals alive at present are the direct descendents of past kinds. Their history can be followed for some 640 million years, and traced back more vaguely to nearly 2,000 million years ago.

The record of the earth for the last 640 million years is written in sedimentary rocks rich in fossils—the remains and indications of animals. The rocks themselves were once separate particles, freed by erosion. They were rearranged by the forces of water and wind, then consolidated under the pressure of later deposits and overlying seas. Layer after layer they have accumulated, the later ones atop the earlier, each with its evidence representing the life of the time it was deposited.

At the Grand Canyon of the Colorado River in Arizona, erosion has cut down through the strata like a saw through the rings in a tree's heartwood. Elsewhere the forces of nature and human activities have exposed fewer levels in one

great succession. A century and a half of studying sedimentary rocks have convinced the geologists and fossil-hunters
(paleontologists) that the record is a single continuous one,
not a series of unrelated episodes.

The oldest of the sedimentary rocks—layers resting on the
underlying volcanic (igneous) rocks and matching their ir-
regularities, curve for curve—are strata exposed in the innermost gorge of the Grand Canyon and atop the Laurentian
hills around Hudson Bay. The most recent of them seem to
have been laid down about 1,590 million years ago. Yet all
of the intervening time has not sufficed to erase deposits of
graphite (a form of carbon) whose distribution and bulk are
significant. No volcanic activity known to science could have
produced these graphite streaks and patches where they are;
but living things that decomposed incompletely could have
done so. As such, the graphite deposits indicate the earliest
known life on earth. From their presence, the earliest sedimentary rocks are described as having been formed during
the Archeozoic Era. Archeozoic means "ancient life." The
graphite deposits are all in the "late Archeozoic."

So far no rocks exposed by today's oceans have been found
to represent the next 200 million years of the earth's history.
Perhaps they will still be discovered under the sea, between
the shore and the edges of the great continental shelves. Or
erosion may have destroyed this part of the record completely. In either case, the gap in history ends the Archeozoic
chapter and leads into a changed world of new sediments,
the Proterozoic Era.

The Proterozoic Era

The strata of the Proterozoic were deposited upon Archeozoic
rocks that had been folded and wrinkled, raised into the air
and lowered beneath the waves time after time. Proterozoic
sediments include additional graphite, apparently of organic
origin, and iron ore deposits that probably represent bacterial
action since they correspond closely to "bog iron" (limonite)

forming today, as well as great accumulations of limestone and a few real fossils. The limestone is so consolidated that no evidence remains to indicate what kind of life may have produced it. But its extent, position, and form do not suggest any other source.

Proterozoic fossils are very strange ones, of algalike plants similar to none known in later times and like none alive today. From studying them, paleontologists have concluded that in the seas where these sediments are there were no plants or animals with bodies rigid enough to make good fossils. There were no woody plants or backbones or teeth. These findings and conclusions are entirely harmonious with the more recent sequence of fossils. Proterozoic means "very early life."

The Paleozoic Era

After the end of the Proterozoic Era about 740 million years ago, no further amassing of sediments occurred for nearly 100 million years on areas now exposed by the oceans. During this interval great changes took place in living things, for the first strata to be laid down some 640 million years ago contain fossils in abundance, many of them of large size. They include animals with armor of many types. The next 390 million years, in fact, are well documented by fossils and are grouped as the Paleozoic Era, with only five comparatively minor interruptions marking off six separate periods called the Cambrian, Ordovician, Silurian, Devonian, Carboniferous, and Permian.

The Cambrian period lasted about 90 million years, from 640 million to 550 million B.C. Its sedimentary deposits are crisscrossed by the tracks and trails of soft-bodied creatures moving over and through the fine silts and oozes on the bottom of shallow seas. Fecal pellets remain as further evidence of these animals that sifted the sediments for food, scavenged for the dying and the dead of larger size, or acted as predators—eating one another.

Microscopic life made few fossils but must have served as the food for hordes of marine worms, shell-less mollusks, primitive crustaceans, trilobites, early sea scorpions and various echinoderms. Jellyfish made impressions in the mud, and fossilization has preserved fragments of free-drifting feathery colonies representing a now-extinct type of coelenterate, the graptolites. Whole "meadows" of stalk-supported lamp shells (brachiopods) filtered the sea water for food particles. So did sponges and various now-vanished types of echinoderms, whose globular bodies rested on rocks or nodded on short stems anchored in the bottom ooze.

Trilobites were creatures of the Paleozoic Era and no other. They became extremely numerous and varied by the end of the Cambrian, and continued as the most conspicuous arthropods until fishes appeared in the seas. Each trilobite had two deep creases lengthwise on its segmented oval body, marking off a left-hand, center, and right-hand lobe—those referred to in the name trilobite. The animal crept or ran or swam with about twenty-four pairs of jointed legs, four pairs of them below the shieldlike head and the rest below the segments of the body. Apparently the trilobites scavenged over the sea bottom, especially among the underwater meadows of seaweeds, sponges, and lamp shells.

Sea scorpions frequented muddy shorelines, feeding on smaller creatures there. Probably they included trilobites in their diet. Sea scorpions were arthropods, too, and followed the same procedure as modern kinds—molting the hard outer shell and growing to a size larger before a new shell became firm. Great numbers of the shed plates were preserved in the fine sediments of Cambrian seas, often as piles of debris swept together by ocean currents. Many specimens remained sufficiently whole, however, for the form of the body to be learned.

Sea scorpions (eurypterids) were limited to the Paleozoic, but reached their greatest numbers during the middle Paleozoic—the Silurian and Devonian periods. Some of them grew to be the giants of all arthropods, with heavy bodies as much

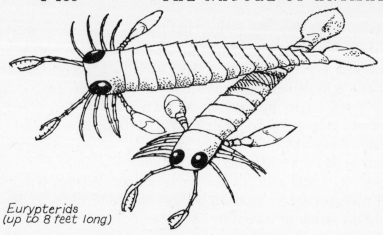

Eurypterids
(up to 8 feet long)

as ten feet long. Their appendages were all at the anterior end of the body, and included paddle-shaped swimming organs, legs useful in crawling along the bottom, and a pair of arms ending in pincers near the mouth. The abdomen was wide at the front, but generally tapered to end in a tail spine suggesting the stinger of a scorpion.

The kinds of animals absent from the fossil record of Cambrian times are as important an indication of conditions as a list of those present. No land animals are represented, and no land plants either unless spores from the Lower Cambrian strata of the Baltic, described in 1949 by the Russian investigator S. N. Naumova, prove to have had this origin. The marine life included no coiled snail shells, no crabs, no tooth or skull or vertebra that might represent an animal with a backbone. The only conclusion possible is that the world in those days was populated rather densely in the oceans with algae and invertebrates.

Sedimentary rocks of the Ordovician series follow those of Cambrian times, and represent the next 75 million years, up to about 475 million B.C. In these rocks are many "firsts": the earliest known corals, chitons, coiled snails, clams, nautiloids, sea urchins, sea lilies, vertebrates, and land plants. The nautiloids were mollusks that seem to have been ancestral to today's chambered nautilus. Those of Ordovician time had straight conical shells, each constructed with a series of compartments comparable to those in the handsomely coiled shell of the modern nautilus.

The vertebrates were all limbless, jawless members of the group to which today's lampreys belong. The Ordovician cyclostomes, however, were flattened, armored creatures called ostracoderms ("shell-skinned"). Apparently they sucked bottom sediments into their round mouths, and digested out the organic matter. But whether they lived in estuaries and lagoons, or migrated between the sea and fresh water (as modern lampreys do), or lived in fresh water and occasionally were fossilized after dying and drifting to the sea has never been settled. Probably their armor protected them from attacks by predatory sea scorpions. Many of these arthropods, in fact, appear to have progressed upstream into freshwater environments before the end of the Ordovician; there some sea scorpions made the further step to land, climbing out into the swamps for brief periods as the earliest known land animals.

The next period of Paleozoic time, the Silurian, is represented by strata lying irregularly over the Ordovician sediments wherever both are found in the same locality. In the seas of the Silurian a number of new animal types appeared: reef-forming corals, sea stars, giant sea lilies, and the ammonoid mollusks—relatives of the nautiloids. The partitions between successive chambers in the ammonoid shell met the shell itself in complexly wrinkled lines that were characteristic for each species; nautiloid partitions joined the shell proper in a smooth circle. Ammonoids with plane spiral shells came to include some twelve feet across before the group as a whole became extinct some 90 million years ago.

Silurian time is believed to have included the years between 475 and 435 million B.C. During this period, jaw-bearing fishes appeared. They lived in fresh waters, and represented a big step forward for the vertebrates. Now animals with a backbone could be active predators, able to bite. Indeed, some of these new types moved downstream into the seas, and there made new use of muscular jaws and sharp teeth. They could dine on limy shellfish such as clams, snails, and lamp shells, or on the less armored trilobites and the young of sea scorpions. Trilobites declined rapidly in numbers soon after jaw-bearing fishes arrived in the oceans.

The Devonian period (435 to 335 million B.C.) is known as the "Age of Fishes," for they were the dominant life of fresh waters and the seas. Some fossilized fishes from the Devonian are as much as thirty feet long, with great biting jaws. Others had lobelike fins, or whole rows of fins along the sides. Some were cartilaginous fishes, comparable to modern sharks and rays. Most were bony fishes.

A number of new types of life appeared in the record of the Devonian period. Among them are the ancestors of to-day's horseshoe crabs. The most spectacular changes of the time, however, came in fresh waters and on the land. Lungs were developed both by freshwater snails and by a group of lobe-finned fishes that appear ancestral to the amphibians.

The land surface exposed during the Devonian appears to have been mostly arid, but pockets of marsh supported a land vegetation composed of spore-bearing ferns, club-mosses, and horsetails, some of them as much as three feet high. Among their bases crept a few rather simple insects, some spiders, scorpions and centipedes—the earliest known representatives of each. Seemingly these true land animals provided an edible incentive for the amphibians to spend adulthood in air, too.

Remains of life from the next 60 million years—Carboniferous age (335 to 275 million B.C.)—are more meaningful to mankind because they furnish the tremendous coal deposits for which the period is named. For some reason the land level fluctuated, bringing inundation and death to marsh vegetation, then re-emergence and fresh growth. Layer after layer of plant material became compressed under conditions that stifled decay, producing coal.

The Carboniferous is often known as the "Age of Ferns" because separation of coal seams frequently reveals beautiful prints of fernlike fronds. A majority of these fossils actually represent the seed ferns which had become widespread after their appearance in Devonian times. They were trees, but very slender ones and feeble in comparison with clubmosses, tree ferns, and horsetails which had trunks 100 feet high and two feet in diameter at the base. Probably far smaller vegetation provided the great bulk of plant debris that became coal. Among the low kinds near the ground were the earliest known conifers.

This new wealth of vegetation formed a paradise through which a great variety of insects walked and hopped and flew. Most of them were cockroaches or members of orders that did not survive beyond the end of the Paleozoic Era. Only a few of these insects were of types with a pupal stage. Some of the Carboniferous fliers were huge. The shales of the period include the remains of pre-dragonflies with more than a two-foot wingspan.

No doubt the abundant insects provided the chief food for hordes of amphibians. The latter reached a dominant position among land creatures. A few kinds of amphibians even invaded the oceans, as ferocious enemies of fishes. Presumably they returned to ponds at breeding time and went through tadpole stages there.

A new branch of the vertebrate line appeared in the Carboniferous: reptiles, although none of them like any alive today. They competed with the amphibians for insects and apparently managed extremely well for, toward the end of the Carboniferous, the tables were turning, the amphibians in obvious decline and reptiles growing much more common and diverse. Whether the reptiles attacked the amphibians vigorously, or some other change brought about the extermination of so many amphibian lines may never be known.

With the sixth period, the Permian (275 to 250 million B.C.), the Paleozoic Era came to a close. The final 25 million years were times of great upheaval, when the Appalachian mountain chain rose above North America. Regions that had been swamps became deserts, and conversely, placing great stress on the ability of living things to change and adapt themselves to new conditions.

During the Permian the giant horsetails and clubmosses came to an end. Amphibians continued to give way before increasing numbers of reptile kinds. Beetles appeared among the insects, as the order whose members seem to have attacked the seed plants so vigorously that both the flowering habit (making use of animals in pollination) and fruit production arose. Today, beetles are the most numerous in kinds of all insects, and insects comprise two-thirds of the species in the animal kingdom; consequently the appearance of beetles was an historic event in the earth's past.

Even the sea creatures were affected by Permian events. The ostracoderms, the trilobites, and the sea scorpions disappeared entirely. Horseshoe crabs dwindled in number of kinds, leaving only a few to carry on into the present as "living fossils."

For an interval of perhaps 55 million years after the end of the Paleozoic Era, no known sedimentary rocks were formed on land exposed at the present time. During this interval, the creatures of the oceans, fresh waters, and continents continued to change in unknown ways that laid the foundation for a great "Age of Reptiles," the 125 million years of the ensuing Mesozoic Era, the earth's time of "intermediate life."

The Mesozoic Era

Early in the Mesozoic, the reptiles acquired adaptations that let them raise their bodies above the ground, supported on four legs or running on two while using the tail as a counterbalance. Some of the smaller land forms were true dinosaurs. Others, such as the ichthyosaurs, invaded the sea and developed streamlining that let them paddle rapidly in pursuit of fishes. A few were of whalelike proportions, although reptiles and not mammals.

By the middle of the Mesozoic, some of the famous giants among the dinosaurs had become established: the "thunder lizard" *Brontosaurus,* as much as 80 feet in length, waded through the swamps, its extended neck supporting a relatively tiny head; armored *Stegosaurus* lumbered along, its back protected by heavy triangular plates in a double crest and its tail studded with the tremendous spines bigger than crowbars. Carnivorous *Allosaurus* must have been a particularly terrifying dinosaur; it stood 14 feet high, and ran on its hind legs in pursuit of prey or while fighting over a mate. Smaller reptiles with wings, the peterosaurs, flitted about; they were so numerous they must have acted like sparrows.

The Cretaceous period (115-75 million B.C.), with which the Mesozoic Era ended, saw one great group of animals after another grow diverse, develop giants, and then vanish. The reptiles reached the peak of their dominance, with such famous members as the three-horned herbivore *Triceratops,* the huge predator *Tyrannosaurus,* and the flying pterodactyls with their leathery wings. The ammonoid mollusks seemingly went wild in making shells with outlandishly complex partitions, in great disks as much as 12 feet across. Yet

Stegosaurus (30 feet long)

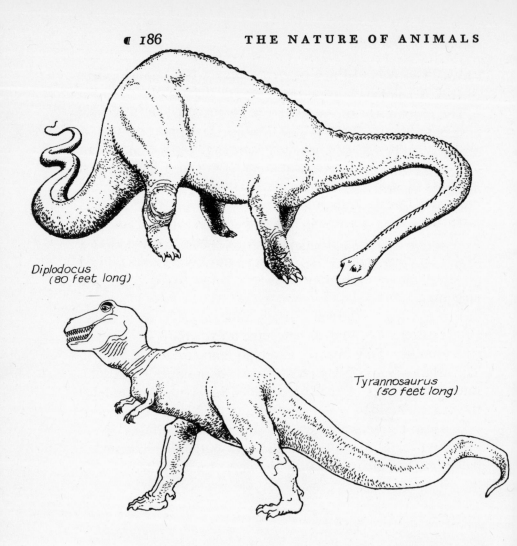

Diplodocus
(80 feet long)

Tyrannosaurus
(50 feet long)

neither the dinosaurs nor the ammonoids survived beyond the Mesozoic.

Tremendous upheavals of the land occurred in Cretaceous times. The Rocky Mountains and the Andes rose up, and the climate changed slowly toward cooler weather and more arid conditions on the land. Yet, by the end of the Mesozoic, the first true frogs and salamanders were replacing the previous types of amphibians. Warm-bloodedness was probably well established, for there are remains of birds—all of them toothed and with long tails feathered on each side, as is seen in the famous *Archaeopteryx* and *Archaeornis*—and an assortment of pouched mammals (marsupials) somewhat like modern koalas and opossums.

The marsupials appeared first in North America, and took advantage of land bridges to spread through the Alaskan area into Asia and downward to Australia on the one hand, and into South America on the other. Still later in the Cretaceous, Australasia—Australia, New Zealand, New Guinea, Celebes, and a number of smaller islands in the East Indies— with its stock of marsupials began its long period of isolation from the rest of the land masses of the world. South America also became separated, but the divorcement was far shorter and the fauna and flora there today are correspondingly less unique.

Triceratops (30 feet long)

Archaeopteryx

The first placental mammals appeared toward the end of the Cretaceous, and it is clear that all of the major orders of insects had become established. The partnership between insects and flowering plants was in operation, with pollination accomplished principally by beetles, butterflies, moths, flies, and bees—all of them insects that go through a pupal stage.

The fossil record is more complete in Cretaceous times than in any earlier period because the gum from pine trees hardened into amber, much of it containing whole insects and spiders, flowers and bits of foliage that got caught on the sticky surface and were preserved under a continuing flow of gum. The insects are as perfect as though embedded in modern plastics. Every bristle is in place.

The Cenozoic Era

A mere twenty million years or so served to separate the Mesozoic from more modern times. Yet by the beginning of the Cenozoic Era about 55 million years ago, the world's animal life had come a surprisingly long way toward its present forms.

These animals promptly faced a succession of geological upheavals. The Rocky Mountains became eroded and then were elevated freshly. The Sierra Nevada were formed, and the Colorado River cut Grand Canyon. The Alps and the Himalayas (including Mount Everest, highest of all) developed from below sea level to greater than their present height. Then, from the Arctic and every mountain peak in the Northern Hemisphere, glaciers crowded down over America and great areas of Europe.

The earliest of the Cenozoic rock formations, the Eocene (55 to 35 million B.C.), is full of fine fossils, including great quantities of amber. Insect remains in Eocene amber are so extensive, in fact, that more is known now of this group of animals in Eocene times around the Baltic Sea than of any other group anywhere as shown by the fossil record. Most of the insect specimens are still representatives of simpler groups, without a pupal stage, although the other orders are present, too. Ants, bees, and wasps of the Eocene are much like those of today, without belonging to modern genera or species.

Eocene mammals were less often insect-eating than were those of the Cretaceous. Most of them had become herbivorous or preyed on larger animals. Many of the herbivores were armored in a way comparable to the modern rhinoceros, or fleet of foot and long of leg, more like modern deer. Small horselike forms appeared for the first time, and also elephant-like, bearlike, and ratlike mammals. Whalelike animals lived an amphibious life at the sea shore, apparently escaping into the open water when pursued on land. Bats flew about, and fragmentary remains suggest the first lemurlike primates.

After the Eocene came the Oligocene, a period of sudden diversification among mammals. The remains of cud-chewing ruminants outnumber all other mammalian fossils, although none of them are clear-cut as deer or camels or cattle. The famous saber-toothed cats appeared in the Oligocene, their enlarged canine teeth apparently well adapted to penetrating the thick, armored hides of the larger, slower herbivores. Porcupines turned up in Africa, and later in South America and North America. True whales swam in the seas. Yet the piglike, beaverlike, and elephantlike land mammals still lacked the distinguishing features of modern pigs, beavers, or elephants. A few jawbones and teeth seem to indicate the presence of primates.

In the Miocene period (20 to 8 million B.C.), which followed the Oligocene, the climate became cooler. The fossils represent perhaps 50 per cent of the modern groups of animals. Saber-tooth cats were bigger than before, and the elephants larger and more elephantlike. The first satisfactory fossils of primates came from Miocene sediments: *Proconsul* was gibbonlike, and *Dryopithecus* more apelike.

In Australasia and in South America, the marsupials of the Miocene reached new heights of development, with catlike, doglike, and other highly adapted forms. North American fossils of the time include rhinoceroses, camels, and tapirs. The mastodon, with its four tusks, represented the elephant group in northern North America at the end of the Miocene, although what it found to eat in sufficient quantity remains a mystery. In Europe, the hoofed mammals included deer, many antelopes, and various giraffelike mammals. Seals and walruses appeared, and whales reached a peak of diversity never equalled in any other period.

The ensuing Pliocene period brought still cooler weather, with greater growth of grasslands. On broad prairies and steppes, grazing animals such as wild cattle, goats, and sheep became abundant in temperate parts of Europe and Asia, although America lacked representatives of these groups. On American plains, horses and camels browsed. The mastodon spread into South America over a new land bridge that permitted a great host of placental mammals to invade the southern continent for the first time. Simultaneously the opossums and armadillos moved northward. At this stage, South America even had marsupial saber-toothed cats. But the competition with placental mammals became too severe, and soon the marsupials largely vanished from the Western Hemisphere.

The growing cold drove many of the cud-chewing mammals from Europe into Africa, and limited to the hardier kinds those that used a new land bridge between Siberia and Alaska. Some of the birds came along. Crows and jays flew and hopped in search of food and nesting sites all the way from the Old World to the Argentine. With them part of the way came the chickadees; America today has 42 different races of these little birds, as compared with about 300 kinds and subkinds still in Asia and Europe. Chickadees have not yet reached beyond Mexico.

How much of the past one million years should be regarded as a final period in the Cenozoic Era, the Pleistocene, depends upon whether modern times (the last 30,000 years) are merely another respite between successive advances of glaciers. Ice sheets made the Pleistocene the "Ice Ages," for they advanced four times, with a major inter-glacial season between the second and the third. Perhaps they will come again.

Early in the Pleistocene the Alaskan-Siberian land bridge was a two-way gangplank. Across it from the Old World to the New came bison and mammoth, the one to multiply into enormous herds on our central plains, the other to become extinct. In the other direction, horses and camels trekked from the land of their origin into Asia and then Africa. The zebras of the African savannas today are little horses that walked thousands of miles—right into the mouths of lions.

During the Pleistocene a double bridge linked North America with South. The first span joined the higher northern parts of Mexico to the mountain country of Central America. The second span persists as the narrow, twisting isthmus of Panama, providing a land highway for animals to South America. Camels used these bridges, too, and their Pleistocene travels from North America to more distant lands account for the modern distribution of camel kinds: the one-humped beast of burden in Egypt, the two-humped dromedary of northern Afghanistan and the Caucasus, the llama and alpaca and silken-haired vicuna in the Andes of South America.

For much of the Pleistocene, North America afforded homes for comparatively few birds. South America, by contrast, had a great wealth of feathered life. As the glaciers receded about 30,000 years ago, South American birds began spreading northward. This sharing has continued, but its rate can be seen in the fact that today, Ecuador has nearly 21 per cent of the world's birds—nearly 1,800 different kinds —in a country with less area than Texas.

From this southern center, the Panamanian bridge acquired (as it arose from the sea) more kinds of birds than the whole of North America, although Panama is smaller than the state of Maine. Through Central America, the gradual decrease in numbers continues. On the Caribbean side,

Costa Rica has 400 species of birds, Guatemala 200, and Mexico 150, although the climate and food available to them seem almost constant. These figures show merely that many birds spread a short way. Fewer went farther.

The Pleistocene saw the extinction of the mastodon, of the saber-toothed cats, of the giant Irish elk *Megaceros*, the ground sloth *Megatherium*, and the giant armadillo *Glyptodon*. Yet in this adverse environment are found the earliest relics of human and subhuman primates, indicating the beginning of man. One of them, probably Cro-Magnon man, is responsible for cave drawings of mammoths and giant elk, of saber-toothed cats and great herds of European bison, none of these being animals that survived into the really recent "Age of Man."

Descent with Change

That so much of the world's past history can be reconstructed from the rocks and the fossils in them is a great tribute to the patience and perseverance of paleontologists. These men readily rebuild a dinosaur from a pile of bones, after each fragment has been freed painstakingly from the rock entombing it. It is far more difficult to match the dinosaur with its eggs, its young, its tracks, the imprint of its skin on mud that hardened into shale, or to recognize its droppings and gizzard stones. All of these correlations depend upon the very finest kind of detective work.

Today it seems incredible that fossils remained such an enigma until a century and a half ago. Yet earlier scientists had no better explanation than the widely held beliefs: that fossils were animals that had been struck by lightning; or creatures drowned by the great flood that Noah and his family survived to describe; or mistakes of the Creator—animals that "didn't work" and were discarded, as though upon a rubbish heap.

Now it is clear that the life on the earth has progressed, descended with change after change. It has evolved. Colossal numbers of animal kinds fell by the way, without descendents. The process is continuing, with additional animals becoming extinct. New kinds are appearing, too, by processes that are orderly and in accord with modern understanding of heredity.

These truths need no longer be guessed at, as was the case at the beginning of the nineteenth century when Jean-Baptiste de Lamarck proposed the idea of evolution and offered a little evidence in support. Not until a good explanation for the process itself became available did the factual side have much appeal. And for drawing attention to the underlying principles, Charles Darwin and Alfred Russel Wallace will long be remembered. To commemorate their clear statements, a centennial celebration was held in 1958, reminding the world that only a century had elapsed since these fundamental conclusions were reached.

The principles themselves are simple. Firstly, it is evident that normal reproduction gives rise to more individuals of each kind of animal than there are space and food for on earth. This leads to a struggle for survival—the survival of very few indeed from each new generation. Secondly, no two individuals are completely identical because ordinary sexual reproduction insures variation. Some individuals are less able to compete for food and mates than their close kin. Inevitably, the poorer adapted individuals leave fewer offspring.

In this struggle for survival, each inheritable feature is tested repeatedly. Each mutation is placed in combination with many other little differences that may previously have had no significance. Any useful combination that aids its possessors to leave more progeny is seen as an adaptation. The valuable gain is continued as a heritage in these new lives. Step by step, evolution proceeds indefinitely. It tends to add one adaptation on top of another, and to eliminate features only when they get in the way—when their disappearance is itself an adaptation with "survival value."

These principles rely upon chance in mating and in the

special double division of meiosis to provide endless recombinations of inheritable characteristics, and upon selection among the countless adaptations in the drastic elimination suffered by each new generation. These animals require no guidance, and yet achieve a direction—toward ever-greater complexity. They follow a course that satisfies a requirement for scientific explanations set forth in the fourteenth century by the English Franciscan philosopher William of Occam: "Entities should not be multiplied beyond necessity." In other words, the principles of evolution form the simplest explanation that will account for all of the known facts.

Atavism and Unused Organs

In its development, each individual animal passes through stages suggesting those of its ancestors, as though it were climbing its own family tree. All vertebrate embryos, for example, develop at least a series of grooves on each side of the throat region. In a fish or amphibian these open as gill clefts through which water can pass to the outside over delicate gills. A human embryo shows these grooves at an age of one month. Ordinarily, they are obliterated. Occasionally, however, a human baby is born with one or more slits between the throat cavity and the outside of the neck; remedial surgery is needed. The retention of a gill cleft in any reptile, bird, or mammal is a "throwback" to its ancestral condition. It is an example of atavism (from the Latin *atavus*, an ancestor). In this case it reminds us that in early Devonian times, all vertebrates were aquatic, and that the direct ancestors of reptiles, birds, and mammals probably lived in fresh water.

The bodies of animals remain curiosity cabinets holding a great assortment of remarkable odds and ends left over from ancestral history. The giant whales, which suffocate from their own weight if stranded on a sandbar, retain hidden within their streamlined bodies the bony remains of a hip girdle and hind legs. Not since the Eocene have their ancestors used legs. Yet the remnants are still there. The python has a hip girdle and a pair of tiny clawed toes close to the cloacal opening, where they seem helpful in mating. All other snakes develop limb buds during embryonic growth and then obliterate every trace of paired appendages.

At one month of age, a human embryo has a conspicuous tail, then overgrows it. The muscles and nerve connections remain until after a normal birth.

All of us have muscles capable of moving our ears, although few bother to learn how to control them and give them regular exercise. All of us possess a vermiform appendix near the junction of the small intestine with the large. It is meaningless except through comparison with other mammals in which the appendix region is developed into an elongated pocket (cecum) in which indigestible plant food undergoes bacterial decomposition before being returned to the small intestine for further digestive action.

A surprising number of human babies show another ancestral feature at birth: a full coat of rather long dark hair over much of the body. Although this hair, called the lanugo coat, is shed completely within a matter of hours or days, the parents may be deeply shocked when first they see their offspring. Ordinarily the lanugo falls off well before birth and, along with dead cells from the skin, some amniotic fluid and mucus, is swallowed by the fetus. These materials are digested or remain in the alimentary canal until some hours after birth.

People pay many penalties for changes introduced by their ancestors even as recently as early Cenozoic times. Adaptations have not yet caught up with the habit of walking on legs alone, with body upright. The ligaments holding the iliac portions of the hip girdle to the sacral vertebrae must support the whole weight of a man who is standing, walking, or jumping. If the strain there is increased by carrying heavy packages or by shocking the connection with sudden jolts (as in jumping), the sacroiliac joint may give way, producing backache and intense local pain.

The return of the blood to the heart is more difficult if it must be raised from the feet to chest height in a standing position. The distance is far less when the body is horizontal, supported on the palms of the hands as well as the soles of the feet. Unless the contraction of leg muscles aids the return of blood in the veins, the pressure within the vessels of the lower legs may become excessive. One common result is varicose veins, which threaten to burst through the skin.

Normal people often develop temporary difficulties in their feet if they must sit up during a twelve-hour trip by airplane. Their ankles and feet are likely to swell alarmingly and remain swollen for a few days. Partly this arises because they have no opportunity to lie down with the feet as high as the heart, or to exercise enough. Partly it is because the cabin pressure has been allowed to decrease to about twelve pounds to the square inch (matching an elevation of about 5,000 feet) from the fifteen pounds to the square inch usual at sea level. Without normal atmospheric pressure to help push fluid back into the veins or along the lymph channels, it accumulates—making the feet feel strangely spongy.

"Living Fossils"

Fossil hunters in the last few decades of the nineteenth century searched diligently for "missing links" that would show when, where, and how the various lines of descent had diverged into unlike types. More recently, scientists have become aware how many linking animals have actually survived in restricted localities as "living fossils" all of whose near relatives appear to have been extinct for millions of years.

Marsupial mammals appeared in the fossil record as early as the Cretaceous period of the Mesozoic Era. Presumably egg-laying mammals came still earlier, even though no fossils are known to represent them. Consequently an egg-laying mammal surviving today is regarded as a very special living fossil. The Australasian area has two of them: the duck-billed platypus and the spiny anteater.

Australasia is a refuge, too, for marsupials, and for several other representatives of ancient groups. One of the strangest is the nocturnal lizardlike tuatara *Sphenodon*, living in burrows on islands off the coast of New Zealand. It alone today shows the living structure of the reptile order Rhynchocephalia, a group widespread in Cretaceous times and earlier. *Sphenodon* is especially interesting because it has a light-sensitive, eye-like organ on top of the head in a position where many of the skulls of extinct reptiles showed an opening suggesting the socket for a third eye.

A fish with lungs would be a relic from even farther back, perhaps the Devonian, when the ancestors of present terrestrial vertebrates were acquiring the adaptations that would permit them to live on land. The world today has three different lungfishes—one in Australia, another in Africa, the third in streams of tropical South America. This distribution is repeated again by the flightless running birds whose ancestors apparently never used their wings: the emus and cassowaries and completely wingless kiwis in the Australasian area, the ostriches of Africa, and the rheas of scrub-covered plains in South America. The ostrich is today's largest living bird, weighing as much as 200 pounds. The extinct moas of New Zealand had the same form, and a weight estimated at 520 pounds. This is still less than the largest bird known, one extinct since the beginning of recorded history but presumably exterminated by early man. This fossil form, *Aepyornis* of Madagascar, probably weighed 965 pounds; it may have inspired the stories of the "roc" in the adventures of Sinbad of *The Arabian Nights*.

Tuatara

The lampreys and hagfishes alone represent the jawless limbless group to which the Paleozoic ostracoderms belonged. They are living fossils of far wider distribution. Some of them continue for life with the same method of filter-feeding shown by the immature stages of all. Others become bloodsuckers, attacking fish and sea turtles. Yet their bodies remain comparatively simple, permitting the scientist to visualize better the soft parts of the ostracoderms that appeared in Ordovician seas.

A lamprey retains a cartilaginous skeleton through which runs the remains of the embryo's stiffening rod, the notochord. The brain never achieves more than a succession of three regions, whereas all other vertebrates develop five brain regions by additional subdividing and specializing. The lamprey's head, moreover, is marked above by a small yellow spot where the skin is thin and unpigmented. Below this, atop the brain, is a third or pineal eye comparable to the one in the tuatara *Sphenodon*.

The invertebrate animals include many living fossils. Peripatuses, the "walking worms," link the annelid worms with the arthropods, and represent a form of life preserved as fossils in shales of Cambrian age. The horseshoe crab *Limulus* of America's Atlantic coast and three relatives in the Indo-Pacific survive from a once numerous group; their nearest kin among the extinct arthropods were the eurypterids (sea scorpions) of the Paleozoic.

On muddy shores below low-tide mark from Japan to Australia, the little brachiopod *Lingula* survives. *Crania*, a near-relative that lives in similar places along north European coasts and in the West Indies, shares with *Lingula* the distinction of having survived with little change since the Ordovician. These two genera have a longer fossil history than any others known. A few kinds of chambered nautilus in the eastern Indian Ocean and the waters off Australia's west coast are alone today in representing the great group of nautiloids which were so numerous in Paleozoic seas.

Living fossils are still being discovered. In 1938 the surprise animal was *Latimeria,* the lobe-finned coelacanth fish caught off the eastern coast of Africa, representing a type of life common among Devonian fossils but believed extinct for at least 75 million years.

More recently the news told of *Hutchinsoniella,* a blind little crustacean collected from Long Island Sound, off the coast of Connecticut. Its body proved to be more like that imagined for ancestral crustaceans in pre-Cambrian times than any other shellfish, living or extinct.

In 1957, scientists sorted out several specimens of a little mollusk from samples dredged deep in the tropical eastern Pacific Ocean. Named *Neopilina,* the creature had a low conical shell like that of a limpet, but signs of segmentation unlike anything known in any other mollusk. It held to its shell with five pairs of muscles, each leaving a scar like the marks found inside fossil shells from the Cambrian and Ordovician periods. Its body contained several pairs of excretory organs much like those of segmented worms. Nothing like *Neopilina* is found in the fossil record for at least 475 million years. Probably other ancient types of life will yet be found hidden away in odd corners of the world.

Preludes to Extinction

No one expects more than a minuscule percentage of the supposedly extinct animals of the past to be found surviving

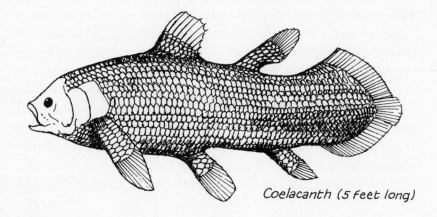

Coelacanth (5 feet long)

today. It is natural to wonder about the very real downfall of all the others. We realize that the different individuals of any single species of creature are unlike in their ability to survive in the struggle for existence. But why cannot each specias mutate and evolve as rapidly as any other species, and maintain its place in the world? It would be interesting to know whether some characteristic leads to extinction, perhaps some feature that might be evident in advance of the disappearance of the last survivor. Presumably any general principle of this kind would apply today as well as in the remote past.

One example after another could be considered: the trilobites, eurypterids, ostracoderms, ammonoids, dinosaurs, saber-toothed cats, mastodons, and mammoths. None of these left survivors. Only the eurypterids and ostracoderms are suspected of being ancestral to any modern kinds of animals.

A clearer case might be seen among the marsupial mammals that seemed so secure in South America. During their isolation from North America they diversified tremendously and fitted almost every possible habit: catlike, doglike, molelike, and many others. Yet, when the land bridge reformed and placental mammals moved southward, only the opossums survived as marsupials in the New World. How was an opossum able to outmaneuver the jaguars, pumas, and many other competitors that stifled all other pouched mammals in South America? Opossums even moved north, and one kind in the past decade has crossed the Canadian border of the United States at several new points.

The answer seems to lie in the opossum's versatility. It climbs, runs, swims, plays dead, bites, and thrives on almost any kind of organic matter, whether plant or animal, alive or decayed. The opossum makes a home in a tree crotch or a hollow log, a vacant groundhog den, or under a farm outbuilding. It is so snarlingly antisocial that, when disaster strikes one opossum, no neighbor of its kind is likely to be close enough to meet the same fate.

In these simple ways the opossum manages to survive. It

regularly wastes all but thirteen of the eighteen to twenty young born a few days after each mating. Only thirteen can be accommodated on the long nipples in the mother's pouch; the other honeybee-sized young die of starvation and exposure. A month later the survivors are able to poke their heads out of the marsupium. They become independent at two months and parents at twelve.

It is highly doubtful that any of the now-extinct South American marsupials were as unspecialized and prolific. More probably they were like Australia's little koalas—ready to perish rather than eat anything but the food to which they were accustomed. Through inability to manage with alternative diets or shelters, an animal shows itself to be overspecialized, excessively adapted, and unable to change in meeting fresh competition.

This pattern is evident among the kinds of animals that today totter on the brink of extinction. The California condor is extremely intolerant of any disturbance within a mile or more of its nesting site, and depends for food upon large mammals dying on range country within soaring range. The ivory-billed woodpecker of southern Florida and western Cuba is correspondingly disturbed by the elimination of virgin cypress swamp forests. The whooping cranes find only a small area of the Texas coast suitable as winter quarters, and breed solely in a remote part of Canada near Great Slave Lake. An invasion of their solitude at either end of the long migration route seems likely to eliminate the last few dozen birds. In each instance, these animals breed very slowly. During the past century their geographical distribution has shrunk progressively at an alarming rate.

Looking into the past, it is easy to conclude that the cold-blooded reptiles that were so dominant during the Mesozoic became sluggish in the chill of late Cretaceous time, and that the active little warm-blooded mammals probably turned to a diet of dinosaur eggs until there were no more.

This explanation is too simple, for there were small-sized dinosaurs as well as *Brontosaurus* and *Tyrannosaurus*. Why did not some of the rat-sized dinosaurs survive, as did the ancestors of today's lizards, snakes, turtles, and crocodilians? If any part of the Cretaceous landscape was wet and warm enough for the survival of frogs and salamanders, why did it not offer sanctuary to older types that became extinct instead? Could some of the flying reptiles not have migrated to suitable territory and survived? Did the carnivorous toothed whales put an end to the great whale-sized reptiles of Mesozoic seas? We do not know the answers.

Where Did It All Begin?

Modern science has become advanced enough to account for many of the life processes of animals in terms of chemistry and physics. The capabilities of protoplasm are now regarded as arising through a long history of added adaptations, as a heritage that is transferred from each generation to the next in the genes of the chromosomes and in the surrounding environment inside each cell.

Where did this all begin? Can the history be pushed backward beyond the first good fossils, into pre-Cambrian times? Is an acceptable explanation available for the appearance of animals large and firm enough to leave a record in the rocks?

For many years these questions have intrigued scientists. Only recently has progress been made toward answering them, chiefly with information on molecular aspects of biology. As never before, attention has been centered on the proteins in living cells. The differences between animals are fundamentally differences in their proteins. The inheritable features, carried in code form in the spiral-ladder molecules of nucleic acids that constitute the genes in chromosomes, spell out what proteins can be synthesized. Proteins serving as enzymes make possible the chemical reactions of life.

With so much attention directed toward proteins, it was natural to inquire whether the amino acids of which proteins are composed might arise from nonliving materials.

Geologists were consulted to learn as much as possible about the atmosphere in pre-Cambrian times more than 600 million years ago, and about the chemical nature of early oceans.

During the Archeozoic, over 800 million years in the past, the earth's atmosphere probably contained chiefly water vapor, carbon monoxide, methane ("marsh gas"), ammonia, and hydrogen, in addition to its present commonest ingredient—nitrogen. Dr. S. L. Miller at the University of Chicago put an artificial atmosphere of this kind into a special glass container with some water, and shot imitation lightning bolts through it to see what would happen. Within a week the ingredients reacted to form several different amino acids in milligram amounts—purely through chance combinations such as could well have occurred in nature. And with no free oxygen to attack them, these amino acids were in no danger of deteriorating.

Protoplasm no longer has any monopoly on synthesizing nucleic acids either. In 1957, a form of deoxyribose nucleic acid ("DNA") comparable to that of chromosomes and a form of ribonucleic acid ("RNA") like that of the respiratory centers of the cytoplasm were synthesized by the physician-biochemists Dr. Severo Ochoa and Dr. Arthur Kornberg in the United States, accomplishments for which they received each a half share of the Nobel Prize in medicine and physiology for 1959.

The question of the origin of life now resolves itself into parts: Could radiant energy passing through the earth's early atmosphere have caused amino acids to form? Might they have combined into proteins, and served as enzymes in the synthesis of nucleic acids? Nucleic acids would be essential to give an inheritable pattern to life. As genes they would control the absorption of important constituents from early seas, and the synthesis of more of themselves—the fundamental requirements for reproduction. Would such teams of genes not been capable of mutation, of evolution? If these are all possibilities, the primitive organization is one that would fit a recent definition of life: a self-catalyzing complex of proteins, capable of self-nourishment, duplication, and evolution.

If the geologists are correct in believing that the earth's atmosphere originally contained no oxygen, the conjectures regarding life's origin can be far simpler. Without oxygen, the amino acids and other organic compounds arising in shallow pools of the sea could be concentrated with no danger of deterioration by oxidation. In addition, the compounds of phosphorus from which an early type of life could get this element—an essential one in all transfers of energy within protoplasm—would have been comparatively soluble kinds, such as phosphites and hypophosphites. No remarkable adaptations of the cell's chemistry would have been needed to acquire phosphorus.

Early forms of life could have been of a multitude of kinds, most of them taking advantage of microscopic size to present to the world a relatively enormous surface in proportion to protoplasmic bulk. In the "primeval soup" of tide pools and the surface waters of the ocean they could find a wide assortment of chemical compounds available as food.

Some of these primitive creatures may have been able to use solar energy. Far more of it would have been available at sea level with neither oxygen nor carbon dioxide in the atmosphere. Ultraviolet and X-rays, both potent in stimulating mutation, would have penetrated in amounts which have no parallel today.

Perhaps a majority of living things in the Archeozoic depended upon the relatively inefficient processes of anaerobic respiration, such as we see today when yeast ferments sugar to alcohol, and bacteria transform the alcohol into acetic acid while deriving energy for their own use.

Even these inefficient types of life could have far-reaching effects upon their world. If fermentation released carbon dioxide into the surrounding water and into the atmosphere above it, a new equilibrium would come into existence between dissolved carbon dioxide and this gas in the atmosphere and precipitated carbonates such as limestone. Today carbon dioxide accounts for 3.1 parts in a thousand of the atmosphere. This trivial amount serves there as a heat trap, helping the earth retain the radiant energy it receives from the sun and affecting the climate at the earth's surface.

With carbon dioxide available, the adaptations leading to synthesis of chlorophyll would permit the modern kind of photosynthesis—combining molecules of carbon dioxide with the hydrogen released from molecules of water, to form a molecule of a carbohydrate. The byproduct oxygen—a carbohydrate molecule of it for every molecule of carbon dioxide absorbed—would be freed into the water and the atmosphere for the first time in the world's history.

It seems likely that these and other early changes brought major crises to primitive organisms. Oxygen, in particular, would bring new conditions leading toward modern times. For one thing, it would combine with amino acids and other organic compounds in sea water, oxidizing them into compounds too simple to yield energy to a primitive organism. Without amino acids and similar materials available, spontaneous generation of life would cease and continue to be impossible—as it is today.

Oxygen would also change the salts of phosphorus from the soluble phosphites and hypophosphites into oxidized compounds that are meagerly soluble. Only kinds of protoplasm able to concentrate and utilize these minute supplies would be eligible for survival. Today's living things are experts at obtaining the phosphorus they must have incorporated into the energy-transfer ingredient known as adenosine triphosphate ("ATP").

With oxygen available, carbon monoxide would transform into carbon dioxide in the atmosphere and in water. Living things dependent upon the monoxide would be replaced by those whose chemical processes permitted use of the dioxide. Some modern plants can use either as the source for carbon, but all are more efficient with the dioxide. Animals of the Archeozoic, if they depended upon plants that became extinct through this change, had either to change their diets or vanish, too.

Oxygen in the atmosphere would soon regroup some of its molecules to form ozone, and a high blanket of this gas would develop gradually, shielding the earth's surface from most of the ultraviolet and all of the X-rays in sunlight. Any forms of life depending upon these radiations for their energy supplies would vanish, leaving as survivors only those with chlorophyll and chlorophyll-like compounds, and the animals living directly or indirectly at the expense of plants. So similar in form are the molecules of chlorophyll and the molecules of enzymes used by animals in respiration with oxygen that evolutionary relationships seem evident at even this level. Probably the whole chemical organization of plants and animals required rebuilding in a series of adaptations matching the presence of oxygen.

These conjectures conflict with no known fact and provide a place for much recent information. They imply that the greatest evolution of all was chemical, and occurred during the Archeozoic Era more than 1,500 million years ago. The structural features that distinguish the many different kinds of animals probably came later, as new adaptations were added. These are believed to include sexual reproduction, increasing variability among offspring, and multicellular bodies, and the various types of skeletal support and coordinating systems that made possible animals of larger size and complex operation.

Probably the general pattern for each of the great phyla of animals became established before many creatures achieved either large size or even the feeble firmness of a jellyfish. Yet animals had to possess some stiffening and attain dimensions visible to the unaided human eye before the mud could retain a trail or a dropping or an imprint that later might be identified as a fossil.

The small number of fossils discovered so far from pre-Cambrian sedimentary rocks fits satisfyingly with expectations. So does the physical structure of the animals represented. But the vast majority must have been microscopic and left no traces of their existence.

Among fossils of Cambrian times, beginning about 600 million years ago, a remarkable number of the animals represented are sponges, brachiopods, and others that filtered microscopic particles from the sea. Predatory habits and the ability to crush a victim became widespread and obvious for the first time among the sea scorpions and the jaw-bearing fishes of the Silurian, 425 million years ago. These active predators developed a relatively new way of life—one that could never have developed until the atmosphere offered oxygen in abundance.

Today the animals that continue to filter microscopic particles from the sea are far less conspicuous than those that swim or run or fly, munching plant food or eating one another. Vigor and freedom evolved slowly but surely. They, too, are evidences of change in both the nonliving and the living environment during the millions of years since animals appeared on earth.

CHAPTER

9

The Spread of Animal Life

❀ ❀ ❀

Recently, the good citizens of Concord, New Hampshire, stood astonished to see the sky clouded by thousands of little birds. It was early autumn. In unheard-of numbers, chimney swifts were congregating over the city, getting ready for their 4,300-mile trip to a winter home in the Yanayaco Valley of Peru.

Many watchers wondered whether the same birds would return next spring. Or would others just like them take their places? More than a century ago, the artist-naturalist John James Audubon was equally curious. Shortly before his twentieth birthday, he tried a simple experiment to get an answer from some phoebes nesting along the Perkiomen Creek where it crossed his father's estate in Pennsylvania. He fashioned light bracelets of silver wire and fastened them loosely around the ankles of five young phoebes in one nest.

Audubon satisfied himself that the markers could neither fall off nor hurt the little birds. Then he waited for spring to begin a search for marked phoebes along the Perkiomen. He found three of the five again. Each had reached maturity and was building a separate nest. Each had gone south for the winter and returned to the same region. Birds definitely do come back to the place where they hatch out and learn to fly.

To find out where birds go in winter, it was necessary to provide many more with distinctive markers. A Danish schoolmaster, H. C. C. Mortensen, improved upon Audubon's experiment by using thin, lightweight metal bands engraved with his name, address, and a serial number. During 1899 he began systematically to attach these to hawks, starlings, storks, and water birds he could trap unharmed and then release. People who found dead birds bearing the anklets returned the metal bands to the schoolmaster. Soon he was able to know the exact routes taken by the fliers in migration.

Other European bird-watchers took up bird banding. By 1904 the method was brought to America and used by Paul Bartsch at the Smithsonian Institution in Washington, D.C., and by P. A. Taverner in Canada. To coordinate these programs in the Western Hemisphere, an American Bird Banding Association was formed in 1909. Within eleven years, so much had been accomplished that the United States Government took over the task, assigning it as an official research project to the U. S. Biological Survey.

Chimney swifts are among the easiest birds to band, for they nest inside chimneys of man's buildings, now that hollow trees are comparatively scarce. By 1943, over 400,000 chimney swifts had been given identifying anklets, but not a single one of them had ever been recovered during the winter time.

In 1944, some Indians in Peru gave a few aluminum rings to a missionary. He sent them to Washington, D.C., as requested by an engraved message on the bands. There the anklets were identified as having been attached to chimney swifts in Alabama, Connecticut, Georgia, Illinois, Tennessee, and in Ontario, Canada. At last the winter home of chimney swifts was known. So far as has been discovered to date, all individuals of this common bird converge from America east of the Mississippi on this one small valley in the remote mountains of Peru.

From recovery of numbered bands, the greatest globetrotter of all has been discovered to be the arctic tern. Many of these graceful birds must travel more than 25,000 miles each year, feeding as they go on fish and crustaceans in surface waters. Arctic terns nest from New England across the polar coasts of the world. But as soon as their young of the year can fly, the whole population sets out for wintering areas in the Antarctic.

One contingent of arctic terns travels from Siberia and Alaska down the Pacific coast of the Americas to Tierra del Fuego. Another crosses the North Atlantic from America to join forces with European birds off the British Isles. These flocks wing southward to the bulge of Africa and there divide. Large numbers continue onward to the Cape of Good Hope, then veer southwestward toward Antarctica. The rest cross the South Atlantic to Brazilian shores, and meet the Alaskan throng at the continent's end. Thence all the terns fan out to feed near the bottom of the world while winter and continuous night close in on the North Pole. Yet, by spring in the Arctic, the terns are back again, ready to raise another brood even if nest sites must be scooped from drifted snow.

Birds that seem to be around all year may actually migrate. The starlings of Washington, D.C., have been found to consist of two different groups. One is in Washington for the winter, and moves in spring to western New York state. At the same time, seemingly identical starlings from North Carolina and Virginia shift into the capital city for the summer. Until large numbers of individual birds were given numbered bands and recovered later, this changing of the guard went on unsuspected.

A variety of migratory habits are evident among the denizens of a forest edge. The bobwhite quail, hatched on the fringe of a field, may never move more than a mile or two from home. With a covey of neighbor quails, it spends the winter apparently unaffected by the goings and comings of other kinds of birds. The catbird travels to the southern states. The wood thrush rarely stops this side of Florida's tip. The redstarts that nest in New England shrubbery search for winter insects either in the larger islands of the West Indies, or fly via Central America to the northern countries of the southern continent. By contrast, the bobolink has barely achieved adult plumage before it is off, by way of Virginia and Florida, "never content" (as Dr. William Beebe put it) "until he has put the great Amazon between him and his far distant birthplace."

Each individual traveler has its own personal destination. Yet the route between the two ends of the trip can vary slightly from year to year. A migrant is an expert navigator, and relies little upon landmarks to show the proper route.

In 1935, Dr. Frederick C. Lincoln discovered broad highways in the sky. This biologist on the staff of the United States Fish and Wildlife Service plotted on a map the information gained from large numbers of banded birds. Each card in a stack before him showed the place where an individual flier had been given its number, and where it had been recaptured—sometimes several times. Dr. Lincoln marked two or more dots for each bird to show where it had been. Then he joined the points on the map with a line.

Soon, patterns became evident. Birds flowed in regular rivers of migration. Dr. Lincoln called these unmarked routes "flyways," and saw that waterfowl, at least, seem tied to a single route for life.

North America has several flyways. One is along the Atlantic coast from Greenland to the West Indies and into South America; it is the route of the blue-winged teal and of large numbers of Canada geese. A second courses along the Pacific coast from Alaska to the tropics, and is followed by the rufous hummingbird along with dozens of kinds of waterfowl. A third flyway funnels down the Mississippi Valley and then skirts the Gulf of Mexico into Central America; more birds take this route than any other, although the blue geese and the snow geese settle for the winter in coastal marshes along the Gulf. The fourth great highway in the blue follows the eastern foothills of the mountains from the Yukon to Texas and Mexico; it is the path of the world's few remaining whooping cranes.

European birds travel in definite patterns, too, and many of them cross the national boundaries of six or seven countries in migrating to their wintering grounds in Africa. Storks from West Germany travel to the delta of the Nile by way of Spain and Gibraltar. Storks from East Germany reach the same area of Egypt around the eastern end of the Mediterranean Sea and Asia Minor.

Asia's flyways stretch across the Equator, often all the way to Australia. Some routes extend to the antarctic continent, and are followed by the few birds that can find suitable conditions there during summer in the Southern Hemisphere.

Birds have no monopoly on migration. Countless numbers of other types of animals travel, too, some to escape cold or drought, others to reproduce in places where they cannot live as adults. To trace these creatures, man has found ways to attach numbered tags and to recover them again at a later date. Millions of fishes now carry serial numbers. Even a sardine is big enough to become an individual to man's eyes in this way.

Young salmon bearing numbered tags descend the great rivers of our western states. In years before great dams were built across the Columbia River, this migration began as much as a thousand miles from the ocean. In the Yukon a young salmon may still travel more than twice this distance downstream to reach Pacific waters. It will be nearing its second birthday and be ready to tolerate salt ocean. Several years later, if living conditions have been good, the same fish may weigh ten pounds or more and be on its way back to its native stream to mate and start off a new generation in fresh water.

From as far as 1,000 miles away, tagged salmon have been

found heading for their destinations, navigating through the ocean in ways no man yet understands. Perhaps 90 per cent of those that go up a river to spawn are fish that went down the self-same route. Six or seven per cent are fish that have wandered in from another tributary of the same river. Only a few have come from more remote fresh waters in their youth.

Walden Pond, near Concord, Massachusetts, is no great distance from the sea. Yet the two four-pound eels that Henry David Thoreau mentioned catching there during his self-exile in the woods, had traveled thousands of miles to Walden Pond. And eels that Thoreau did not capture had an equally long journey before them. Until 1922, however, these migrations remained unknown. In Thoreau's day, no one had even found the male sex of the common eel, despite a deliberate search for it.

The remarkable travels of eels were traced first by a Danish fisheries officer, E. Johannes Schmidt. He proved that eels from both America and Europe mate and lay their eggs deep in the Sargasso Sea, a great eddy in the Atlantic Ocean southwest of Bermuda and north of the Bahamas. Here the newly hatched young rise slowly into surface waters and are whirled northeast by the Gulf Stream.

American eels mature more quickly than do their European kin, and by the time the current has carried them close to the long eastern coastline, they are ready to strike out westward into fresh waters. European eels need eighteen months to achieve a corresponding stage of development. By then the Gulf Stream has carried them to Europe, and they swim up rivers there.

Only the young female eels travel upstream to ponds where they can feed and grow for several years to reach maturity. It was female eels that Thoreau captured. They had almost finished their stay in fresh water. Within a few months, if they had been left to live, each would have ceased feeding and made her way down the nearest stream to the Atlantic Ocean. It is in the brackish water of the estuaries that the

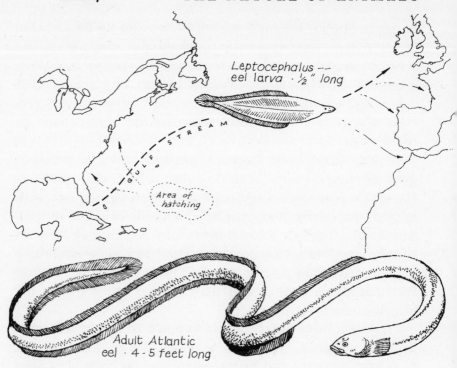

Leptocephalus —
eel larva · ½" long

GULF STREAM

Area of
hatching

Adult Atlantic
eel · 4 - 5 feet long

females meet the males which have matured there without
further migration. In company, the two sexes continue onward to their rendezvous beneath the Sargasso Sea a thousand miles away.

Thoreau prided himself on having "travel'd widely in Concord." The garter snake and the varying hare (or snowshoe
rabbit) which shared with him the shores of Walden Pond
moved about far less than he. They are always homebodies,
rarely venturing more than a quarter of a mile from their
point of origin.

In recent years, naturalists have made these differences
clear by giving distinctive tags to a wide variety of animal
life. No creature is too large and few too frail to yield information. The deer and the raccoon in the forest, the bats
of cave and belfry, the whale and the butterfly have all been
given numbers.

The methods of the bird banders were extended to whaling

in 1926. Special ten-inch darts of stainless steel were shot into the fleshy backs of calves and nursing mothers, giving a means of recognition to whales the whalers do not catch. Each dart bore an offer of "Reward for return to *Discovery*, Admiralty, London."

More than 5,000 whales in waters of the Southern Hemisphere bear these markers every year. From recovered darts it is clear that whales grow faster than had been believed possible. Some reach maturity and a length as great as 77 feet in three years; whalers count on at least a ton of whale for every foot in length. They are also beginning to realize that the sea lore recounted by Herman Melville in the story of Moby Dick may represent the type of migration actually followed by these monsters. Moby Dick was a sperm whale, a type traveling in pursuit of fishes and squids from the North Pacific to the South Atlantic and back, around the tip of Africa in southern summer on one of the most definite sea routes known.

To those who tag animals, butterflies surely represent the opposite extreme. For years, everyone assumed that butterflies flit aimlessly about, with neither destination nor awareness of past course. Then Dr. Frederick A. Urquhart of the Royal Ontario Museum in Toronto, Canada, began fastening numbered labels to the wings of monarch butterflies, inviting anyone who found a marked insect to return its tag. He soon saw that the great swarms of monarchs that congregate along the north rim of Lake Ontario in late September are on their way to Florida and the Gulf States for the winter. Only the females straggle back in spring, arriving almost spent but still ready to wait a week or more for fresh milkweed plants to thrust upward. Then the eggs can be laid where monarch caterpillars will feed to maturity.

The Realms of Animals

In spite of the annual travels of so many mammals, birds, fishes, and insects, the animal life of the world shows remarkable patterns. Flightless penguins swim from antarctic waters to the Cape of Good Hope, to the tip of South America, and to many islands in the Pacific south of Australia. But they do not venture north of the Equator. Nor are polar bears found south of the Arctic Circle. Kangaroos are strictly Australian, and only the American tropics have monkeys that can hang by their tails.

A human traveler who is familiar with the larger kinds of animals on earth can tell quickly not only the continent upon which he stands, but also the particular part, merely from the kinds of creatures around him. He may think of the world as a patchwork of realms, each distinct from all others in its animal inhabitants.

The most unique animals of all are found in Australasia. This vast territory is home to the only egg-laying mammals in the world, and to all of the marsupials in existence, with the exception of a few opossums in America.

Only the bats which fly from Asia, a few rodents that can swim well, and the dingo dog brought to Australia by aboriginal man represent placental mammals long established in these lands "down under." This absence of competition from other mammals has permitted marsupials to succeed in the Australasian areas, where they take the places in nature occupied elsewhere by mice, moles, wolves, and many other types of fur-bearers. Some of the various kangaroos graze on the plains grasses; others climb trees to reach the foliage there. The koala "teddy bear" is the principal marsupial whose local name has become known all over the world. The great assortment of bandicoots, cuscuses, phalangers, wallabies, and wombats are familiar only in the Realm itself.

The famous lyrebird spreads his magnificent tail feathers on Australian soil alone. The continent is home also to the ostrichlike cassowaries and emus. Other special animals of the Australasian Realm inhabit New Zealand or smaller islands. The flightless kiwi, with hairlike feathers and no wings at all, probes the soil at night for earthworms and insects on New Zealand and nearby islands. The many spectacular birds-of-paradise display for mates only in New Guinea.

The parrots of the Australasian Realm include the handsome cockatoos, many of them with feather crests. Cockatoos, in fact, help show how far the animal life of Australia has spread westward along the islands of the East Indian chain. They extend to Lombok, but not to the next bit of land—Bali—just east of Java.

The tiger of Asia is found on Bali and islands still closer to Malaya, but not on Lombok or in any part of the Australasian Realm. Between Lombok and Bali runs an invisible boundary known as "Wallace's Line." It separates Celebes to the east from Borneo to the west, and then turns toward Hawaii as though fencing the Philippine Islands into Asiatic territory. On one side of Wallace's Line the animals are Australasian. On the other, they are members of another great life realm, the Paleotropical.

The position of this boundary was discovered nearly a century ago by Alfred Russel Wallace, a field zoologist of note who became even more famous as co-founder with Charles Darwin of our modern theory of evolution. Wallace saw that the animal life on the Philippines, on Borneo, Bali, Java, and Sumatra was all far more like that of Malaya and Burma than anything to be found on Lombok or islands farther toward Australia.

The Paleotropical Realm is literally the "Old World tropics." It includes all of Africa south of the great deserts, as well as the remarkable island of Madagascar, the mass of India plus Ceylon, the Malay peninsula, and the larger islands of the East Indies as far as "Wallace's Line." In it are found almost all of the world's big cats—lions, tigers, leopards— and all of the anthropoid apes—gorillas and chimpanzees in Africa, orangutans in Sumatra and Borneo, and gibbons in Malaya. It has many monkeys, and all of the other nonhuman primates in existence—the tarsier of the Philippines, the lemurs and their kin in Asia and Africa.

The Indian Ocean cuts the Paleotropical Realm into two

halves, each with an elephant and a rhinoceros or two. The western portion is the Ethiopian region, and contains some of the most extensive grasslands and jungles on earth. The grasslands are home to lions which prey upon antelopes and zebras, while the parklike plains with scattered trees or denser forest give food and shelter to giraffes and big-eared African elephants, to the black rhinoceros and the square-lipped (or "white") rhino, to ostriches and secretary birds. Waterholes and rivers attract hippopotamuses and the dangerous Cape buffalo. Madagascar is rich in lemurs, and the center of distribution for the world's true chameleons.

The eastern portion of the Paleotropical Realm is the Oriental region, where tigers, leopards, monkeys of many kinds, and peafowl (peacocks and peahens) are all found in dense jungles. Water buffaloes live in its swamplands, while the Indian elephant and Asiatic rhinoceroses inhabit more open country.

The Paleotropical Realm and its counterpart in the Western Hemisphere—the Neotropical Realm ("New World tropics")—between them contain all of the world's nonhuman primates. Most of them are in the Old World, but the monkeys are split between the two. Old World monkeys can be recognized by the closeness together of their nostrils, and by their lesser dependence upon forest trees. Baboons and mandrills in southern Arabia and Africa, in fact, have become almost purely terrestrial. The rhesus monkeys of Asia Minor to Malaya, and the Barbary apes of North Africa and Gibraltar, on the other hand, are expert climbers.

New World monkeys are highly adapted to forest life, and many of them use the tail as a fifth hand—a habit found in no monkey of the Old World. The nostrils of New World monkeys are separated by a flat area, as seen among marmosets, the capuchin (or "organ grinder's") monkey, the howler and the spider monkeys.

The Neotropical Realm supports all of the world's true anteaters, armadillos, vampire bats, peccaries, llamas, and other small relatives of the camel, and most of the known hummingbirds, tapirs, and guinea pigs. Its toads and frogs are in remarkable variety, but large animals of ox kind, sheep kind, and horse kind are conspicuously absent. Birds limited to this region include the ostrichlike rhea, the big-billed toucans, and the guanay birds whose excrement is marketed by the Peruvian fertilizer industry.

The rest of the earth's land supports animals of such uniformity that it constitutes one realm, the Holarctic, covering the North American continent north of Mexico, all of Europe, Asia north of the Himalayas, and Africa north of the Sahara Desert. Truly circumpolar animals are found in the Arctic, but their numbers decrease on all continents in lower latitudes: ptarmigans among the birds; walruses, polar bears, wolverines, weasels and ermines, lemmings, varying hares, moose, musk ox and caribou (or reindeer) among the mammals. Farther south the Holarctic Realm is home to almost all of the known bears, foxes, lynxes, marmots, squirrels, bison, elk, deer, sheep, loons, and tailed amphibians.

Often the Holarctic Realm is divided into an Old World half, the Palearctic region, and a New World portion, the Nearctic. The Palearctic is distinguished by the presence of hedgehogs, wild boars, camels, the panda, and the common viper, none of which has any counterpart in the Nearctic. The Palearctic also has a far larger number of kinds of sheep, goats, mice, and rats than the Nearctic, and probably was where man first domesticated the horse.

The Nearctic lacks wild horses and pigs, but is the native home of pocket gophers, jumping mice, muskrats, raccoons, skunks, and rattlesnakes.

To a large extent these great realms of animal life are characterized by the stay-at-homes—the animals that do not migrate. Those creatures that do make an annual trip tend to be like the African elephants, the mountain sheep, and the elk (or wapiti) in changing their elevation on mountain slopes according to the season, or in wandering over a large area as nomads, with the habits of caribou.

Within the broad pattern, changes in distribution occur at

intervals. Since 1900, the nine-banded armadillo of the Neotropical Realm has spread into Texas, eastward as far as Florida and northward into Oklahoma. The coatimundi, a Neotropical relative of the raccoon, has extended its range into New Mexico and Arizona. The crested tanager and the coppery-tailed trogon are birds that have moved north beyond Mexico. And about 1930, the buff-backed heron of Africa crossed the South Atlantic to the New World. There it became known as the "cattle egret" before it spread into the United States and some West Indian islands.

Barriers Against the Spread of Animals

Occasionally it is possible to recognize where a definite barrier is limiting the spread of some kind of animal. One of these is evident at the Cape of Good Hope, where warm southbound waters of the Indian Ocean meet cold northbound waters from the Antarctic, flowing into the South Atlantic along the west coast of Africa. The Indian Ocean and the whole of the tropical Pacific Ocean are inhabited by venomous, fish-eating sea snakes that use their brief, flattened tails in swimming and diving after prey. No snakes of this type are found anywhere in Atlantic waters. Yet only the sudden temperature change seems to keep the sea snakes from rounding the Cape of Good Hope into the South Atlantic.

Cold weather forms a barrier for many land animals, too. Snakes and lizards may be able to hibernate in secluded retreats, but of all the lizards in America, only the little five-lined skink has been able to survive in Canada. There it is limited to the southern part of Ontario, where it is protected from severe winter by the encircling Great Lakes. Alligators apparently cannot find enough to eat during the winter north of coastal Virginia. No reptiles, in fact, are found much beyond the Forty-eighth Parallel, separating many of our western states from Canada.

Lesser animals show these same limitations. The ghost

crab that scampers along the beach so rapidly as to be called the "rabbit of the crustaceans," is at home on sandy shores from Rio de Janeiro to the south side of Long Island, New York. Edible blue crabs roam the shallows and fiddler crabs dig burrows in mudflats as far north as Cape Cod, Massachusetts. Fiddlers are common in the other direction throughout the tropics, whereas the blue crab extends around the Gulf of Mexico only as far as the mouth of the Mississippi.

Until recently, the green crab was regarded as a homebody. It inhabited the shore waters from New Jersey to Cape Cod. Now it has wandered northward to the Bay of Fundy, to the dismay of New England shellfishermen, since it attacks clams just when the demand for them has reached an all-time high.

A desert can be a barrier, too. Animals unable to tolerate drought may not cross from one side to the other. For countless generations they can be isolated from previous neighbors if slow changes in weather and in the earth's shape produce a desert in between.

One island of high land surrounded by desert in America is visited each year by thousands of people who come to see the Grand Canyon in Arizona. The north rim of the tremendous chasm is the edge of the Kaibab Plateau, where squirrels with tufted ears and a slightly different race of mule deer are at home in a magnificent forest of ponderosa pines. These animals are bounded on the south by Grand Canyon, and in every other direction by land that is too arid or too far for them to cross.

The isolation of the Kaibab squirrels and deer developed during the past 50 million years as the plateau rose slowly, a skyward bulge of the planet's crust against the erosive force of the Colorado River. Just as a sharp knife might cut into a grapefruit raised against it, the Colorado has maintained its course for 217 miles across the rising land. Now the north rim with its pines and squirrels and deer is a thousand feet higher than the south rim, and almost a mile above the river. It is enough higher than the land around that more rain falls on the plateau in summer and more snow in winter.

By comparison, the south rim is arid, sparsely clothed in pinon pines, and devoid even of the Kaibab squirrels' nearest kin.

The most isolated animals of all live on oceanic islands. Their ancestors probably reached their present homes as waifs and castaways stranded on unfamiliar shores after perilous journeys, riding rafts or hurricane winds from far away. As though reformed from wandering again, these island animals tend to stay where they are and make the best of it.

The smallest of the world's feathered fliers, the bee hummingbird of Cuba, travels as far as the nearby Isle of Pines but not beyond. Jamaica has three different hummingbirds, one of them the spectacular streamertail "doctor bird," as well as a brown owl and two different kinds of parrots, none of them known in any other island.

On a clear day, the handsome big parrot of St. Lucia in the British West Indies must surely be able to see the French island of Martinique twenty miles to the north, and the British island of St. Vincent a corresponding distance to the south. But no St. Lucian parrot visits Martinique. No parrots do. Nor does the St. Lucian bird wing across to St. Vincent. St. Vincent has its own kind of parrot, a lesser bird but equally a stay-at-home.

These island birds are not tied to the ground, as are so many island insects and the lizards that feed on them. Nor are they lacking in fliers to imitate, for the blue-winged teal and thousands of shore birds from North America use the West Indian islands as stepping stones between wintering grounds in South America and nesting sites in the United States and Canada. Instead, the isolation of island birds is largely self-imposed, as a part of the constitution with which they are hatched from the egg.

Zones of Animal Life

Each of the major continents shows evidences of barriers producing a broad scheme of animal distribution. Preferences for special foods and shelters and for latitudes or altitudes with suitable weather produce life zones lying across North America like diagonal sashes, crumpled only in the western mountains because of the great variations in altitude there.

Those who consider Alaska and the Far North as a land of ice and snow are thinking only of the Arctic-Alpine zone that extends northward from the Aleutian Islands and around the coast of Alaska on the shores of the Arctic Ocean. It crosses northern Canada and covers the area from Hudson Bay to Greenland as a tundra in which the heat from the summer sun is insufficient to thaw the soil to any significant depth. Trees cannot find a place for roots; the tundra is treeless. Low plants, mostly lichens, mosses, sedges, and grasses, support wandering herds of musk ox and caribou. During the brief summer, a temporary burst of plant growth feeds vast numbers of migrant waterfowl and shore birds, as well as the blood-sucking insects that attack them. Farther south on mountain tops, the alpine counterpart of the arctic tundra is home to bighorn sheep and Rocky Mountain goats in summer. To survive, these large animals must descend for winter into more temperate elevations.

The rest of Alaska and much of the Far North is far richer in animals. It lies in a second band across the continent, the Boreal zone, named for the Greek god of the north wind. This is mostly an evergreen forest, limited northward by soil that thaws out in summer and lets tree roots penetrate.

The Boreal zone is inhabited by moose and elk, by porcupines and varying hares, by crossbills and golden eagles. The Canada lynx stalks through this territory, searching for prey well down into British Columbia and as far as the northern Great Lakes and the easternmost shores of the Gulf of St. Lawrence. A few of these big cats survive in a corresponding ring of evergreens below the limit of trees on high mountain slopes.

Most of us live in the Austral zone, named from the Latin word for south. Extending to the tropics, it is the home of our most familiar animals: the robins and blue jays and song sparrows, the woodchuck and gray squirrel and beaver, the white-tailed deer and black bear, the opossum and raccoon. On the plains and in the mountains farther west, it is the native territory for bison and jack rabbit, mule deer and pronghorn antelope, grizzly bear and prairie dog, trumpeter swan and water ouzel.

The tip of Florida and the coasts on both sides of Mexico are truly tropical. Their animals are the northern outliers from the Neotropical Realm. Life in the steamy swamps and jungles seems to have stepped above man's head, leaving the trails he treads empty for most of the day and much of the night. Overhead the animals creep and clamber upon the high branches of the forest canopy, reaching foliage in sunlight that fails to penetrate or cast shadows on the ground.

The stability of these life zones, and even of the major realms of animals, is measured in millennia. During every man's three-score years and ten, he can detect changes, although many of them seem slight. Very gradually a new order replaces the old, and the fauna adjusts itself to fresh challenges in the environment.

C H A P T E R

10

Animals and Mankind

Today the animals of the world face a change affecting them on every continent, one challenging their right to a future. In less than 50,000 years, mankind has transformed from an inconsequential type of primate into the most successful species the world has ever known. Now the other animals must fit, if they can, into environments tailored increasingly by man.

Growth of the human population can be traced long before the beginning of written history. Until the end of the Old Stone Age, about 12,000 B.C., all of mankind depended upon foods that grew naturally—wild animals and herbs. On this basis, about two square miles of fertile hunting territory are needed to support each person. Since the entire earth has only about 20 million square miles of this quality of land, the maximum possible population at the end of the Old Stone Age is believed to have been about 10 million people.

Explorers in the past three centuries have encountered

many tribes still following the way of life of the Old Stone Age. The Plains Indians in America were at this level when first discovered by westward-spreading pioneers. It is clear today that these Indians were at peace with their land, even if not with each other. Their welfare depended upon the seemingly limitless herds of bison. Yet their hunting methods were so primitive that the Indians could not destroy this resource. When bison became scarce in any region, enough Indians starved to bring them once more into balance with their food supply. Without outside disturbance, this economy had an indefinite future.

A sharp rise in human population was made possible through the development of agriculture and the domestication of animals for food. In these ways man began to substitute favored plants and meat animals for the native vegetation and its related, dependent fauna. This increased efficiency in food production went hand in hand with urbanization and division of labor, with one man becoming a carpenter, another a tailor, rather than the head of each family attending to construction of every kind and his wife making the clothes.

By about A.D. 1650, when this stage in the evolution of human habits began to merge with the next, the world's population had grown to about 545 millions. The rise from 10 millions seems tremendous until it is realized that, during more than 13,000 years, the population actually doubled itself less than six times: 10 to 20, 20 to 40, 40 to 80, 80 to 160, 160 to 320, and 320 to just 545 millions. During this period, each doubling of the numbers of mankind took an average of 2,260 years.

The Industrial Revolution that began about 1650 made man with his machines so much more efficient that larger numbers of people could be supported. The population grew to match: 545 millions in 1650 to 728 millions in 1750, to 1,171 millions in 1850, and to 2,400 millions in 1950. In the two hundred years between 1650 and 1850 it more than doubled. The 1950 census figures show that it doubled again in less than a century. If this accelerated increase is maintained—and all the evidence points that way—the next doubling will come even more quickly. The 1965 report by the Statistical Office of the United Nations predicts 7,000 million human mouths to be fed by A.D. 2000.

Each doubling of the human population at least doubles the amount of food needed. In most agricultural areas, food production per acre has not increased at a corresponding rate. Instead, man has extended his food-producing acres by reclaiming land—building dikes and pumping out the sea, as in Holland, or irrigating the desert, as in America and Israel. He has transformed forests into grazing areas and swamps into vegetable gardens.

Man is unique in the degree to which he can change the environment—his environment and that of all the living things around him. Seldom has he introduced changes on the basis of careful study, thoughtfully analyzing the situation he found in a region to learn how it could be modified for prolonged use in another way. Rarely has he considered it important to arrange for a new balance between the native animals and plants, to disturb the wild kinds as little as possible. Instead, he has taken away land from them. Many have become extinct, or restricted to small areas—a few of these set aside in recent years as sanctuaries. Other animals have become camp followers, as pests despised by everyone. Between these two extremes the majority of animal kinds still continue precariously, their futures unpredictable as man comes to occupy progressively more of their world.

Primitive man tends to regard other animals as his kin. As he acquires means to kill animals and dominate plants, this point of view changes. He then tends to regard living things as divided between two categories: the useful and the useless. Theologians of the Middle Ages believed firmly that the universe had been created for man's benefit alone. So egotistical a concept is hard to support from modern scientific evidence. Yet people living in cities, whose realization of the ultimate sources of food extends scarcely beyond the shelves of the supermarket, tend to agree with the philosophic scientists of the seventeenth century, who suggested that man might at least discover some use for every living thing.

Useful Animals

Certainly a vast number of different uses have been found for animals and their products. High on the list of valuable kinds, certainly, would come sheep, cattle, pigs, domestic fowl, ducks, geese, and various types of fish whose muscle tissue is so valuable as protein in human diets. Game animals are more luxury fare. So, in many regions, are shellfish.

All manner of animals are regarded as food in specific parts of the world: grasshoppers and caterpillars in Mexico, beetle grubs in equatorial Africa and Australia, octopus and squid around the Mediterranean and the western Pacific, sea cucumbers along Oriental coasts, sea urchins in the West Indies and various parts of Europe. The need for meat, whatever its source, is worldwide. An inadequate supply is the basis for a widespread dietary deficiency known today as kwashiorkor. Small wonder, then, that the word for almost any animal to natives in much of Africa can best be translated "meat."

Animals contribute little to man's need for fuels, light, and power. Yet the conventional measure for power is horsepower, and the use of the various domesticated animals for traction and for turning mills extends from sled dogs and caribou in the Arctic, through horse, ass (burro), mule, elephant, camels, to water buffalo, llama, and others. In desert and semidesert areas, where trees are scarce, dung is used for fuel. Whale oil for candles lit man's night activities for years, and gives us a unit of illumination—the standard candlepower. The "oil sardine" was caught in early times to furnish fuel for lamps, including the classic form so often depicted as the "light of reason"—the one by which ancient scholars studied when "burning the midnight oil."

Perhaps the largest product of animal activity useful to

man is found in the oceanic islands ("atolls") of the South Pacific, where coral animals have built reefs upon which land plants now grow and people make their homes. In other parts of the tropical world, coquina rock is used as a house-building material; it is a limestone consolidated from coral fragments, the tubes of worms, and bits of mollusk shell. Marble is a fine-grained limestone, consolidated from a more remote past.

Man sees value in other animals because they contribute to his technology. Warm waters are home to several kinds of sponges with skeletons that are flexible and marketable. The squidlike cuttlefish of the Indian Ocean provide cuttle-bones, such as are hung in cages with pet canaries as a source of lime. Ink from these jet-propelled relatives of the octopus, sold as "India ink," used to be one of the most reliably water-proof materials known; now "India ink" is usually a synthetic product.

The use of plastics has diminished somewhat the impor-tance of freshwater mussels, from whose shells "pearl" but-tons can be cut. Commercial "mother-of-pearl," on the other hand, is an extract from fish scales.

Increasing use of nylon and other synthetic fibers has af-fected the silk industry, wherein silkworms (caterpillars) are fed on mulberry leaves and provided with clean quarters in which to spin their cocoons. Later, cheap hand-labor un-ravels the cocoons and prepares the fiber for use as thread. So far, however, none of the artificial products has replaced spider silk for the cross-hairs in the eyepieces of surveying instruments; collecting it is a limited and highly specialized industry. Similarly, down feathers have not been satisfac-torily supplanted as the insulating material in sleeping bags, or wool from sheep and goat as a fiber for warm clothing.

The economic value of furs and feathers is appreciated widely. Tortoise shell, and the skins of various lizards, alli-gators, and snakes, like the hides of ostriches and some mammals, have a considerable commercial importance as decorative and utilitarian materials. Perfumes are based on highly malodorous secretions from the musk glands of the skunk and other mammals, and on ambergris, a substance obtained from diseased whales. Even the excrement of animals is useful to man: manure from domesticated kinds, and the guano of sea birds and bats. Guano from islands off the Pacific coast of South America supplies not only the fertilizer needs of many countries, but is a source of phosphates and nitrates as well in the manufacture of explosives and other chemicals.

We tend to remember the honey produced by bees as a contribution to human diets, but to forget the far greater benefit these and other insects confer by pollinating the flowers that precede the fruits we enjoy. We think of earthworms as useful bait in angling for fishes, and overlook the fact that they are merely the conspicuous members of a great community of soil animals whose activities are part of the decay of organic matter, yielding simple compounds a plant's roots can use. We enjoy the smaller birds for their songs and colors, and give them less than their fair credit for destruction of weed seeds—an activity in which wild mice are important, too.

Predatory Animals

It is easy for man's feelings to be biased in relation to the larger predatory animals. He sees the hawk or fox that takes a hen from the chicken run, but not the hawks and foxes that keep rats, mice, rabbits, prairie dogs, and grasshoppers under control. He finds evidence of the wolf or coyote or mountain lion that attacks a domestic animal, and often is unaware that the individual these predators destroy may be already sick or dying. Instead, he visualizes his loss as of a prime animal ready for the market, whether sheep or calf or colt, and tends to condemn all predators of the kind for raiding human food supplies. Only the scientist who examines the stomach contents of hundreds of predators knows how much benefit these animals confer on man by limiting the number of herbivorous insects and mammals that otherwise would destroy vast amounts of the grains, vegetables, fruits, and forest trees raised as crops.

While raising food, man confronts his environment more consciously and consecutively than in most other activities. He sees comparatively little that he can do to protect his crops from torrential rain or occasional drought, from frost or burning sun. But predators that raid his livestock become personal enemies he can destroy. In his anxiety to get quick results, to make his land into an outdoor factory yielding its maximum of products, he may show no regard for the food web linking all the local animals and plants together.

So often a cattle rancher, pioneering in western America, has found a mountain valley of startling beauty, its grassy bottomland grazed in summer only by deer and elk. He moved in with his herds, shot a few deer and elk for his table, for doeskin and elkhide and decorative antlers, and noted with some relief that the rest of the wildlife had taken to the surrounding hills.

From the mountain slopes beside frontier ranches, an occasional bear or family of wolves came to raid the live-stock now grazing on the valley floor. Mountain lions attacked the horses, while bobcats and coyotes took a toll of sheep. The rancher set out with traps and gun to eliminate the predators, and by persistence, succeeded rather well.

In this oft-repeated situation, however, the rabbits and mice and rats prospered without interference by predators. They quickly overran the valley and interfered with growth and reproduction of the grasses upon which the domestic livestock depended. In the mountain forests at the same time, the shy deer and elk reproduced unhindered by their natural enemies. The rancher and his friends shot a few, but made no attempt to keep up with the growth of deer and elk populations.

Each winter the food supply in the mountains failed to support so many animals. Some starved. Others subsisted by standing on their hind legs to reach low branches of the trees, or chewed the bark for the nourishment it contained.

The forest developed a "browse line" and no new under-growth survived. Older trees died because bark had been removed all the way around the trunk, girdling them.

The typical rancher worried only because deer and elk, rabbits and mice invaded the bottomland pasture in unheard-of numbers, and served as an attraction for predators from beyond the mountain rims. Perhaps poisoned baits could be spread in such a way as to eliminate the wild herbivores without endangering domestic livestock.

Often the rancher noticed that, in spring, the girdled trees on the mountain slopes failed to leaf out. The sun melted the snow quickly, and spring rains drained down the mountain slopes in torrents that spread sand and mud over the valley pastures. Then the water was gone. Streams dried up. The grasslands became dormant by mid-summer and, for the first time, the rancher found himself having to buy fodder for his stock during a normal growing season. He grew apprehensive over the danger of fire on the mountain slopes, now that so many of the dead trees were tinder-dry. Among the sun-crisped woods, occasional porcupines chewed on the blanched skeletons of deer and elk, for these animals had died in thousands.

Year after year in this typical situation, the yield of the ranch shrank, the costs of maintenance rose. Grasses of kinds the livestock enjoyed tended to die out from over-grazing. Thorny shrubs spread unchecked, although they had been rare when first the rancher saw the valley. Gradually the earlier beauty waned and was replaced by the sere harshness of a highland desert. Few predicted that elimination of the predators at the top of the pyramid of life would have let the plant-eaters destroy the mountain vegetation and the valley pasture, too. The rancher, whose economic world collapsed in this way, so often added sorrowfully: "It was fate. I couldn't do a thing to prevent it!"

These problems are world-wide. In Africa, men sought to protect the native women who went to the rivers for water and to wash the laundry, taking the children along. The men eliminated the crocodiles which previously had attacked people; crocodile meat and leather were valuable by-products of this police action. But, as the crocodiles were killed off, the nearby gardens became plagued with wild pigs and rats; people were attacked by cobras and pythons; all of these wild animals were able to drink now in safety at the rivers, survive, and reproduce. At the same time, the economically important food fishes, such as the freshwater korper *Tillapia,* became scarce. Armies of land crabs, now freed of control by crocodiles, ate *Tillapia* eggs and fry. Catfish and lungfish, both favorite foods of crocodiles, increased, too, and attacked the catch in fishermen's nets, often tearing the nets as well. In Madagascar, the elimination of the crocodiles was followed by spectacular increases in the number of stray dogs and in the difficulty of controlling outbreaks of rabies.

Herbivorous Animals

In Australia, New Zealand, and many of the world's smaller islands, man has sought to improve the availability of meat by introducing European rabbits. They multiplied, often without hindrance, and soon overran the areas open to them, spreading to new ones wherever possible.

Rabbits competed successfully with domestic livestock, five rabbits eating as much as one sheep. In Australia, sheep production decreased in spite of thousands of miles of supposedly rabbit-proof fence erected at public expense, plus vigorous campaigns of trapping, shooting, fumigation of burrows, and the introduction of European predators. Domestic cats went wild, but could not eat rabbits as fast as rabbits reproduced.

In the 1930's and early 1940's, Australia and New Zealand supplied most of the world market for rabbit fur to be made into felt products, and shipped millions of frozen carcasses annually to any country whose citizens had a liking for rabbit pie or stew. Meanwhile, the introduced predators did more to eliminate the native ground-nesting birds and the

marsupial mammals than to control hopping rabbits. Re-
duction in the number of birds and insect-eating mammals
let insects multiply. Suddenly the eucalyptus trees, for which
Australia is so famous, began to lose their leaves, partly
through caterpillars and partly because boring beetles had
invaded the tender branches. Australians saw koalas exposed
among the branches, each koala trying to find some foliage
the insects had missed. To save the eucalyptus forests, men
began exterminating the koalas.

As recently as 1950, the Australians were counting rabbits,
aware that the unmolested progeny of each pair could have
about 13 million offspring in three years' time. Just when
almost everyone had given up hope of correcting the great
mistake—introducing rabbits in the first place—scientists
tried out a suggestion from South America. They liber-
ated experimental rabbits inoculated with myxomatosis, a
virus disease of Brazilian rabbits. At first nothing happened.
But in the summer of 1951-52, Australian mosquitoes began
transmitting the myxoma virus at an amazing rate. Rabbits
sickened and died as never before. At least 995 out of every
thousand rabbits on the continent disappeared. Pastures grew
lush again. Quality of mutton and wool rose spectacularly.
And by the time rabbits with an inherited immunity to the
introduced disease began appearing, the human inhabitants
of the "down-under" lands had decided on all-out campaigns
to rid themselves of the survivors. With resourcefulness and
hard work, the people may succeed.

As the Australians and New Zealanders learned, and as so
many ranchers found in the western United States, it is far
easier to upset the balance so precariously maintained between the members of a food web than to restore it after-
ward. A new balance may be reached in less than a century,
but it is likely not to be to man's liking or to serve his plans
as well as the earlier state of affairs.

Often man is surprised to see that a major change in animals in an area alters the landscape as well. Lighthouse
keepers whose islands became overrun by European rabbits

found that the extensive burrows honeycombed the shores, letting them collapse and erode away as much as eight feet a year—shrinking the island at a visible rate. African villagers, who rejoiced when a government hunter was appointed to shoot for them a hippopotamus each week as a community meat supply, could not understand why rainy weather began to bring floods that inundated gardens and homes as well. They failed to believe hunters who insisted that hippos were needed to keep the river channels open and let the water through.

Before these interactions between man and animals in a changeable environment were understood, many an attempt to conserve a vanishing resource led to fresh disasters. President Theodore Roosevelt foresaw no difficulties in 1906 when he created the Grand Canyon National Game Preserve in Arizona. His goal was the perpetuation of a magnificent herd of mule deer and the forested plateau on which they lived. This natural deer park is bounded on three sides by mile-deep canyons, and to the north by the semi-desert lands of Utah. As a game preserve it would be a paradise for deer.

President Roosevelt's action led to the removal of some 30,000 sheep, 20,000 cattle, and thousands of horses that stockmen had been pasturing on the area. The program of predator-elimination begun by the stockmen was continued, however. Until 1931, the hunters and trappers continued their work, killing 816 mountain lions, 30 wolves, 7,388 coyotes, and 863 bobcats on the sanctuary plateau.

The deer herd multiplied. From about 5,000 animals in 1906, the number rose to 40,000 in 1918, and 100,000 by 1924. The deer outstripped their food supply and, during the winter of 1924-25, about 60,000 of them died of starvation. The next winter another 36,000 suffered the same fate.

The combination of repeated starvation winter after winter and long-delayed action by officers of the Forest Service brought the mule deer herd to about 10,000 animals by 1939 —one deer for each sixty-eight acres of the sanctuary land. Slowly the trees have recovered since that time, and the plateau regained much of its original charm. Thousands of visitors who pass through the area on their way to experience the thrill of Grand Canyon from its north rim, do so without realizing that they are in the home of the first large native wild animals to draw man's attention to the importance of predators in controlling the lower levels in the great pyramid of life.

Control of Pests

The web of life is full of equivalents. What wolves and mountain lions are to deer, keeping them under control, the parasites and predators of smaller size are to the caterpillars and beetle grubs, the grasshoppers and other pests that attack man's crops. Frequently, the appearance of a new pest merely demonstrates that man's former allies have fared badly, perhaps because of some action he has taken.

Until chemical sprays for codling moths eliminated predatory insects as well as moth caterpillars from America's apple trees, orchardists had seen no evidence of damage by red spider mites. Then, while entomologists sought new insecticides to rid the trees of mites, the codling moths evolved new races immune to the original types of poison. For production of marketable apples it makes little difference whether the fruit is ruined by caterpillars or mites. Many an apple grower has concluded recently that his best allies are not the spraying machines but the chickadees and other birds that hunt out insect eggs in winter, and the wasplike insects that parasitize caterpillars.

The gnats and mosquitoes that annoy man (and carry diseases to which he is susceptible) can evolve into types affected only by insecticides dangerous to many other kinds of life. Tolerance of man-spread poisons is no help to these insects, however, in evading bats and dragonflies and swallows that hunt out each victim. The small predators, moreover, change in numbers according to the amount of food. In a "good year" for insect pests—a "bad year" for man—

the natural enemies of gnats, mosquitoes, caterpillars, and mites have plenty to eat and reproduce rapidly, providing increased control that becomes combined with the effects of diseases in bringing the pests once more into balance. On the other hand, of course, a tropical storm may kill large numbers of swallows or bats on migration between their winter homes and the northlands where they feed all summer. Subsequently the northern insects, now freed temporarily of predators, may reproduce in a major outbreak.

Occasionally, man is so impressed by the assistance given him freely by other animals that he commemorates the event. In the square around the main Church of Latter Day Saints in downtown Salt Lake City, Utah, is a memorial to the gulls that swept down upon the crickets plaguing the first crops of the Mormon pioneers. The birds seemed heaven-sent; they arrived just in time. Actually, they came from nesting sites on islands in Great Salt Lake only a few miles away, and fed on the crickets at this season quite regularly. They are one of the factors in the food web, keeping fat-bodied "Mormon" crickets from overrunning the countryside.

Vanishing Wildlife

Upon rare occasions the human race has shown regret over the disappearance of a species it has shoved to extinction. On May 11, 1947, the Wisconsin Society for Ornithology dedicated a monument to the extinct passenger pigeon. This memorial in Wyalusing State Park was unveiled some thirty-three years and eight months after the last living bird of this kind died in the Cincinnati zoo. In the wild, passenger pigeons have not been seen since 1907.

Men still live who can remember the roar of pigeon wings as thousands of frightened birds took off from a roosting site. Or the way an aerial armada of these fliers would blot out the sun in passing. Yet no one is sure today exactly which of man's activities ended the possibility of survival for the species. Was it the number of cartloads of dead pigeons brought as food to the cities by market gunners? Was it the loss of nesting sites in the great beechwoods of America as these were felled to make room for homes and farms? Was it the substitution of crop plants of interest to man for native vegetation upon whose fruits the passenger pigeon depended? Was it a mild disease of domestic birds, spreading to the wild species and eliminating them? No one can ever learn the answer.

The decline and extinction of one kind of animal after another has troubled many people. Reductions in commercial catches of fish were so marked in American waters that a United States Fish Commission was organized in 1872 to study the situation. Depletion of migratory birds and larger mammals became evident soon afterwards, and a Biological Survey Commission was appointed in 1896 to investigate and recommend legal measures that might save dwindling species.

Private citizens, too, were concerned over the rapid destruction of wildlife. In 1905, many banded together into a National Association of Audubon Societies for the Protection of Wild Birds and Animals, Incorporated. Little by little these organizations enlisted support among the general public and legislators, In 1940, the two federal agencies were combined into the United States Fish and Wildlife Service. The private association became known simply as the National Audubon Society. Together they stand for the passage and enforcement of laws in the interests of animals.

More than 45,000 square miles of the United States have now been set aside from commercial use to save threatened kinds of creatures from extinction. Over 28,000 square miles are in patches known as National Wildlife Refuges; they are managed as havens or as breeding grounds. Our National Parks, although totaling slightly less in area, are left unmanipulated and consequently afford sanctuary to a wider variety of wildlife and native vegetation. A fox that attacks nesting ducks can be eliminated on a National Wildlife Refuge in the interest of more ducks. In a National Park the fox has as much right to the ducks as the ducks have a right to live. Both are left in as near a state of nature as can be contrived with the public welcome to come and watch.

In spite of protective measures, many conspicuous kinds of animals are tottering on the edge of extinction. Probably less than twenty ivory-billed woodpeckers—the second largest woodpecker in the world—remain in the last shrinking wilderness areas in southern Texas and western Cuba. The population of whooping cranes rises and falls slightly, earning newspaper headlines every year. In 1968, it was up slightly, with forty-eight wild birds under observation, and another twenty-two in captivity. The California condor may number only thirty birds, and the Everglades kite no more than fifty.

Our national bird, the bald eagle, is in desperate straits, too. Illegal shooting, destruction of nest trees, and inability to reproduce due to eating foods contaminated with insecticides, are all blamed for the fact that the bird has disappeared entirely from many states in which it was formerly a conspicuous and thrilling sight. An estimated one thousand pairs remain.

Of the world's mammals, the closest to extinction may be the antelope known as the bubal. The last census of these animals in North Africa recorded only twenty-five individuals. A sanctuary in Java contains the last thirty rhinoceroses of the island species; they are still in grave danger from poachers who covet the horns, for these can be converted into a powder with a high market value because of its reputation as a love philter. In the Gir Forest of India are about 100 Asiatic lions, the sole remnant of a once widespread kind. The smallest deer in the world—the diminutive key deer now restricted to Florida's Long Pine Key—may number no more than ninety-five individuals. This is about equal to the number of European bison remaining; but all of these bison are under constant observation in zoos. The sea cow or manatee of Florida's coastal swamps may not survive much longer; less than 200 are known to remain.

Sanctuaries

A few kinds of animals have profited from protection. The American bison had all but disappeared in the wild when, in 1889, the United States Government decided to purchase the survivors. A century earlier the widespread herds may have included anywhere from 50 to 100 million bison. Less than 600 survivors could be found—an eighth as many as "Buffalo Bill" Cody had killed in a single year. These few bison were given sanctuary, and their descendents now comprise great herds in the National Bison Range of Montana, the Wichita Refuge in Oklahoma, and Yellowstone National Park in Wyoming. Today's captive herds total more than 5,000 individuals, living almost as they did before the white man came.

The record with some waterfowl is almost as good. A series of crises had brought the population of the largest of all—America's trumpeter swans, with a seven-foot wingspan—crashing to a mere seventy-three in the United States in 1935. About 1,500 now exist, many of them in the Red Rock Lakes National Wildlife Refuge set aside in Montana primarily to conserve the species.

The little goose that serves as the official bird of our newest state, Hawaii, has recovered somewhat from its depleted condition of a decade ago. Then a mere thirty individuals could be found. The néné (pronounced nay-nay) has reproduced both in the wilder parts of some Hawaiian islands to a total of perhaps fifty free birds, and also to a population exceeding 150 in zoos, especially the Severn Wildfowl Trust sanctuary in England. The néné's living requirements are being studied in the hope that a suitable sanctuary in Hawaii can be provided to ensure a future for this goose.

The riddle in all conservation of wildlife is whether a large enough area can be set aside as a sanctuary, and protected from all outside demands. The Montezuma National Wildlife Refuge, sole large resting place for migratory waterfowl in New York state, was cut in two and its value largely destroyed to save a few million dollars by routing a toll road through the middle. In Illinois, the Crab Orchard Lake Refuge for birds following a migratory path along the Mississippi flyway was taken as the site for a new federal prison. And in Oklahoma, the usefulness of a great research refuge was largely eliminated because the U.S. Army insisted on using a corner of it as a firing point for long-range guns. Only in 1958, when these weapons became admittedly obsolete, did this interference cease.

To let a community of wild animals and plants proceed with their evolution undisturbed by man requires solitude that is both hard to find and harder to provide. This is evident in the largest wildlife reserve in the world—famous Kruger National Park in the Union of South Africa. The 7,340 square miles of parkland there represent an area about equal to the whole of Massachusetts or Israel.

Kruger Park is a long rectangle, some 200 miles from north to south and only 40 miles across. The unfenced boundaries are irregular, and extend for more than 500 miles—too much for the small force of rangers to patrol. This means that an animal has only to walk 20 miles to pass beyond the boundary into farmlands on which it can be killed legally as meat. And when a poacher comes in to trap or shoot game, he need not go far. Part of the boundary is international, between Mozambique (Portuguese East Africa) and the Union of South Africa, and includes wild country difficult to police from either side. Huge as Kruger Park is, its elongated shape makes it too small to be properly effective.

Kruger Park resembles many another sanctuary set aside for animals. It is crisscrossed by narrow roads upon which people drive to see the lions and zebras and antelopes, particularly during the dry season. By then the herbivorous creatures have eaten most of the foliage remote from the roads and are migrating slowly, either to their death beyond the park limits or toward the roads. The animals have learned to ignore the cars, and impala—the most abundant antelope in the park—often hold up traffic as they cross by the hundreds.

The lions in Kruger Park have evolved a new method of hunting based upon the presence of cars. They slink along beside a vehicle, while its occupants shiver in delight at being so close to a wild and dangerous predator. When the car and lion reach a herd of impala or zebra, the big cat rushes from its concealment in the vehicle's moving shadow to pounce on a victim. This is scarcely undisturbed nature, but it is enough to satisfy the visitors who drive slowly along the roads.

Uses for the Land

As the human population of the world increases, man's sense of values changes, too. With machines doing more of the work, he has gained time for leisure. Many people now regard unspoiled scenery, wild animals, and native plants as among the things they wish to see in leisure time. They find an esthetic pleasure in the out-of-doors, a comforting contrast to city living. To satisfy these needs, America has already set aside about one half of one per cent of the country's land in parks and monuments, and preserved a slightly greater area in national forests. These are a heritage in which the welfare of wild animals and native plants are given special consideration, and the beauty of particularly striking landscape is preserved intact.

At the same time, ways are being learned for multiple use of land—taking from it a crop of trees or food while providing a place for the animals. Conservation of soil, production of crops, and the welfare of native wildlife can all go hand in hand if man plans properly.

So long as man continues without plans, upsetting food webs, and providing no working substitute, he destroys the soil, causes silting of the streams, reduces production of food, and brings to extinction one kind of creature after another. Mismanagement of the land means pollution of fresh waters and of the coastal regions of the oceans. This, in turn, curtails the reproduction of fish and shellfish alike, seriously reducing the amount of food available to man. Aquatic life can become extinct, too, to man's irreparable loss.

So far as science can see, the animals and plants alive today are the ancestors of all the living things this earth will ever have. Every kind that dwindles out of existence reduces the number of types for which man might eventually find a use. No matter how valuable a dodo or a passenger pigeon might be, there is no way to have a live one now. Nor any of the descendents which could have evolved into still different birds.

Efforts to reverse the downward trend in the number of animal kinds on earth, and to provide a place for plants man regards as useless at present, often require international co-operation. This too can be done well. Just as world peace among men is worth working for, so, too, is a harmonious relationship between mankind and the other living things on the planet earth. The sooner this harmony is achieved, the more man will have earned the name he has borne for three centuries as one member of the animal kingdom. He named himself *Homo sapiens,* "the wise man." Now, as never before, he needs urgently to demonstrate this wisdom. For as long as man exists on earth, he will hold both the power to dominate all other life and the responsibility for wielding this power well. Wisely he can insure for all plants and animals, including himself, a long future as wonderful as the past.

Index